Gulf Stream

SOUTH FLORIDA'S
LITERARY CURRENT

number 22
2004

EDITORS
John Dufresne   Cindy Chinelly

EXECUTIVE EDITOR
Diane Mooney

ASSOCIATE EDITORS
Christine Caya
Melanie Neale

FICTION EDITOR
Christine Caya

NONFICTION EDITOR
Jill Drumm

POETRY EDITOR
Jill Drumm

ADVISORY EDITORS
Lynne Barrett   Denise Duhamel

ASSISTANT EDITORS
Andrea Dulanto   Richard Ryal

Cover Photo: Terri Carrion
Back Photo: Eric Vichich
Cover Design: Acropolis

Produced by the Creative Writing Program
Florida International University

Submissions must be previously unpublished and accompanied by a
short biography. To submit electronically, visit our website
(http://w3.fiu.edu/gulfstrm) for directions. Hard copy submissions
should include a stamped, self-addressed envelope. Reading period:
September-January1. $5.00 sample issue / $15.00 year subscription.
All correspondence should be addressed to:

Gulf Stream Magazine
English Department-FIU Biscayne Bay Campus
3000 NE 151 Street
North Miami, FL 33181-3000

Gulf Stream is funded in part through an endowment given in memory of Stanley Barnett.

Gulf Stream

SOUTH FLORIDA'S LITERARY CURRENT

CONTENTS ◆◆◆◆◆◆◆◆◆◆◆◆◆◆◆◆◆◆◆◆2004

PHOTOS

CONTRIBUTORS' NOTES   116

Poetry Contest

Only unpublished work considered

1st Place - $250 and publication in Gulf Stream
2nd & 3rd Place - Notation and Possible Publication

Judge: Campbell McGrath

Campbell McGrath is the author of five volumes of poetry:
*Capitalism, American Noise, Spring Comes to Chicago, Road Atlas,
Florida Poems,* and his newest collection, *Pax Atomica,* due
out December 1, 2004.

GUIDELINES:
$10 for five poems and $5 each additional poem
(check or money order - NO CASH)

Name should not appear anywhere on manuscript

Include cover page and short bio as well as
SASE for notification

Deadline is December 1, 2004

Entry includes a one year subscription to Gulf Stream

Address Entries to:
Poetry Contest
Gulf Stream Magazine
English Dept. - FIU Biscayne Bay Campus
3000 NE 151st St.
North Miami, FL 33181-3000

Make Checks Payable to: Gulf Stream

Coming Spring 2005

Gulf Stream Issue 23

Dennis Lehane

An excerpt from his new novel
Babe Ruth in Ohio

Also Featuring
The 2004 Mystery Fiction Contest
Winner
Selected by Judge Barbara Parker

Murder, We Write Les Standiford

In the 1920's, the writers all went off to Paris and became known as the expatriates. In the late 1950's, the poets were hanging out in North Beach and Berkeley, the novelists had taken New York, and the most interesting among them were known as the "Beats." Now, as the millennium turns—apparently these things cycle every half-century or so—there's another literary center and another group of writers scribbling away: genus, *Florida*; species, *Mystery Writer*.

It is arguable that Florida, at least the southern half of it, boasts more crime, thriller, and mystery writers per capita than just about anywhere else in the country. There's Carl Hiaasen, James W. Hall, Edna Buchanan, Randy Wayne White, Tim Dorsey, Paul Levine, Barbara Parker, James Grippando, Sterling Watson, Carolina Garcia Aguilera, Vicki Hendricks, Christine Kling, Dave Barry, Jonathon King, Stuart Kaminsky, and Cherokee Paul MacDonald, not to mention yours truly. Elmore Leonard spends half the year down this way and sets a similar portion of his work in these parts. Dennis Lehane may not have written a Florida mystery novel yet, but, as an F.I.U. alum, he certainly trained here.

Although, sadly, John D. MacDonald, and Lawrence Sanders and Charley Willeford, who gave us Hoke Moseley, and Doug Fairbairn (*Shoot, Street Eight*) have all left us, their work still is issued and swells the *ouvre* significantly.

As for proof that interest among book publishers remains keen, consider this: just a few short years ago, the *Miami Herald Tropic Magazine* commissioned a spoof, a serialized mystery novel jestingly titled *Naked Came the Manatee,* to be penned in weekly installments by a number of those already named, among others. Within days, and long before the first word saw newsprint, three major publishing houses heard of the venture. They entered into a bidding war that escalated well into the six figures, for the rights to reprint what was essentially an extended joke within hard covers.

How to explain it? As my F.I.U. colleague James W. Hall likes to say, Florida history, especially South Florida history, can be divided into three periods: 1) before Miami Vice, 2) during Miami Vice, and 3) after Miami Vice. It's not only a good joke, it is incisive commentary on what is going on here. The television series (*Saturday Night Fever* on a Donzi, as one wit dubbed it) not only revolutionized the look of American television, but ingrained, world-wide and forevermore, the image of danger, double-dealing, and flash flourishing in the Florida paradise.

But it's more than an accident of television programming. Were it not for the dozen or so who are writing these books, it seems that the place itself would have squeezed out a different set of writers to bear witness to the era. Readers are captivated by the beauty here, as they are by the irony and by the tragedy of experiencing violence in such paradise. And it goes deeper.

As were New York and Southern California in other eras, Florida has become *the* American entry point, the focal frontier region where immigrants stream in to settle, clash, and clamor, up against all the interests that have been established before them. It is, above all, a place on the edge, where everything is up for grabs, where nothing has yet been decided, where the conflicts and the co-minglings presage that which is to come for America as a whole.

When an addled Miami waiter, befuddled by business setbacks and at loggerheads with the IRS, hijacks a bus full of school children and demands to be taken to Joe's Stone Crab Restaurant, the pathos of the American Dream is laid out at a glance. When the lady bus driver and a police SWAT team foil this sad plan—on live television, no less—the public is reminded of the valor of which all citizens are capable. And when the school-children are delivered into safety, we are reminded of why we all struggle for a foothold. All of this in one South Florida morning's lead story.

Such events occur elsewhere, but nowhere else with such poignancy. Florida's beauty represents paradise. Its open portals signify promise. The attendant and seemingly inescapable violence portend the difficulties faced by a nation which has been living on the come since the first days of the Republic.

But the flip side is the sense of possibility that's palpable in the Florida air. There's a freshness here, a sense that no group is firmly in charge, that one person's dreams are as good as anyone else's, and just as likely to come true. In the stories that follow, you'll see this freshness embodied in a variety of subjects and styles and stances.

In one way, the reports that reached Ponce de Leon a few centuries ago were correct: the streets in Florida *are* paved with gold. It's just that there is always somebody scheming to pick it up as quickly as it gets laid down. If you don't believe me, just turn the page.

Les Standiford
Miami, September 2004

Les Standiford is Director of the Creative Writing Program at Florida International University and author of a dozen books and novels, including Havana Run, Last Train to Paradise, *and the forthcoming* Meet You in Hell: Andrew Carnegie, Henry Clay Frick, and the Bitter Partnership that Transformed America.

Everybody Loves Jim Preston Allen

For the killer, night brings no sleep.

There is the darkness, and in it lurk the shadows that dance. The specters and ghouls. The spirits in the shape of lamp, bureau, and mirror gothic. The silence without is not loud enough to drown the noise within. The killer lies in bed sorting out the noises in her head. Her lips move. She is counting in English. An hour passes. Her lips continue to move. She is counting in Korean. The babble in her head is loud tonight. Tonight there is singing amid the cursing.

Let's dance, Let's dance to the drummer's beat, Let's dance, Let's dance to the sound so swe-e-eet. You bitch, then shoot me, you mothafucking bitch, let's get this shit over with, let's, let's, let's, Let's dance to the sound so swe-e-eet.

The killer's lips move. She is counting in Spanish. She glances at the glowing clock. 5:46. Almost time to get up. She calculates that she has slept less than an hour this fleeting night. Time to get up. Already. The doctor says the problem can be solved with pills. They are salvation in the outline of a small, unopened tube on the bureau. She does not believe in pills. She believes in a strong will. If your will is strong, you can accomplish anything, even sleep.

Then, her lips cease to move. The noise fades, the singing and cursing, as she drifts into sweet sleep. Her alarm screams. 6:00 already. She stirs, groggy, not believing how sleepy she is. Now. Oh, delicious sleep. Why now? Her lids are heavy. She hugs the pillow. Why now, when at last the noise in her head is on mute? She reaches to silence the alarm and decides she will not rise today. She will not stir. This will be her day to sleep. She crawls under her pillow and draws her knees up to her chest. She is buried in a hole of cool darkness. It is quiet in here. In here, the dead are not singing. She is asleep at last.

＊   ＊   ＊

It is an hour later, though it seems like mere minutes, and now the phone begins to ring.

"Oh, damn."

She is groggy, her body still heavy with the joy of sleep. She should not answer the phone, but she reaches for it out of something like a sense of duty. She knows who it is. She will explain about the sweet sleep, which she has earned. They will understand. They must.

"Hullo?"

"Where the hell are you? Get in here."

"No," she says. "Calling in sick."

"Time a the month?"

"Fuck off, Lambert."

Lambert says, "They found him. Last night."

"Oh, shit."

"Found him right where the girl said he would be."

"DNA?"

"Still working on it."

"Where's the pig?"

"Sighted up by the Indians," Lambert says. "You want some of this or what?"

"I want some," the killer says. She is already out of bed. Sleep, and the need for it, have been pushed aside by the rush of adrenaline. She is wearing her sleeping clothes: boy shorts and a jog bra. Her legs are long. They are strong, like her arms, from the gym and Tae Kwon Do. Her skin is black, even blacker than the night. She is checking her gun as she says into the phone shouldered to her ear, "Quick shower. See you in fifteen."

"Skip the shower," her partner says.

"Right," the killer says. "See you in ten."

"You're really not gonna bathe? That's kinda nasty." She can feel Lambert's sick grin through the phone. "But I kinda like it. A woman's natural smell, and all. Unwashed brown sugar is still so sweet."

"Fuck off."

The killer registers her partner's laughter as she hangs up the phone. It was only a joke, but it has unsettled her. She enters the shower with her head full of shame.

He said *sweet*, not *swe-e-eet*.

He is already at the Indian casino waiting by his big car, smoking a cigarette. He is outlined in a halo of light from the sun coming up. He is a pudgy angel in a tacky jacket. His mouth falls open in a smile when he sees her. His lips are thick, his fingers are thick. He used to be sandy blond, but he's going gray and bald. He favors the comb over. He's not much to look at, but he's a good partner. He holds his own. The other one, the one she favors?

She says to him, "Where's Sosa?"

"Couldn't make it." Lambert grins. Maybe he's thinking about Sosa, bent over a toilet puking up his guts. Maybe he's checking out her figure in the black bodysuit and silver, steel-toed boots. He looks her up and down. That toothy grin on his face. "Sosa is sick," he says.

"Sick?"

"Drunk."

She eyes him. "Did you call him?"

"I swear I did. His old lady said he's . . . sick. Out cold." Lambert is laughing.

The killer shakes her head at Lambert's cynicism. You gotta trust your partner. You gotta trust who's got your back. "He could really be sick, you know?"

Lambert grunts. She's always defending her beloved asshole Sosa. He points to the entrance of the casino. "The pig's been in there twelve hours straight. Security says he hasn't even taken a few minutes to eat or piss. He's loaded. He hit yesterday at the track. He's banging that machine at twenty bucks a pop without blinking. I got two of the boys in there scoping him. Can't figure how we're gonna get him out here, though. There's close to five thousand people in there still. We go for the takedown, it could get messy, especially if he's got a gun. The Indians don't want that. We could wait out here, but who knows how much money he has on him. He could be in there another couple hours banging a big wad like that." Shrugging, he turns back to her. "You hungry? Want breakfast or something?"

"I want him."

She is already on her way to the casino entrance.

"The fuck are you doing?" Lambert says. "We don't got jurisdiction here. This is Indian land!"

She turns and shows Lambert her gun. "This is all the jurisdiction I need."

"But we can't go in there."

She is entering the casino. Her beautiful black clad backside is framed in the doorway. The valet parking attendant takes notice, smiling. The rotund Seminole Indian sheriff takes notice, smiling. The tough dyke Seminole Indian security guard takes notice, smiling. Maybe it's her steel-toed silver shoes. The killer disappears inside. The doors close.

"Jesus K-Rist. Jesus K-Rist." Lambert is talking into his hand held fast. "Sosa, Sosa! Wake your ass up. Sosa! Our girl's gone ballistic again."

Let's dance
Turn that music down, sir.
Let's dance
I said turn that music down.
Let's dance to the sound so swe-e-eet.
Turn that damned music down!
Okay, okay, okay, detective. But you've got nothing on me. Because I didn't do anything. Really, I'm telling you the truth. I loved that boy. Fact of the matter is, I did. (I'll tell you one thing, though, you are beautiful. Do you know that? You are so sw-e-eet.

Is it all right if I tell you that?)

Asshole!

Okay, okay, I was outta line. Don't lose your cool. We're all innocent til proven guilty. Ha-ha-ha. What was your name again? M. What kind of name is M?

Fact of the matter is, there was a single mother of two, a blond boy of thirteen, a brunette girl of twelve. Well, the brunette girl was more than brunette, she was more what you would call interracial, which took nothing away from her personality, which everybody said was sweeter than sugar. Swe-e-eet. And this single mother, she was, well, nothing could be taken away from her just because she was twice a mother and never married and one of her kids was from a black guy who would never see the light of day because he was in prison on death row. This single mother, to meet her, everybody said, was to understand that people could have a good heart and yet make bad decisions one right after the other. Fact of the matter is, she was wonderful, this single mother, everybody loved her. She took care of her old parents while her better-off brother and sister (a doctor and a business woman) didn't. She raised her two kids in a clean home, though it was in a trailer park. She made sure they did good in school (straight A's, both of them). And she gave them both a healthy dose of religion, which the boy especially took to, because he was born with one leg shorter than the other and had to wear an ugly orthopedic shoe. But she continued to make these bad decisions concerning men. Seems like, because her youngest child was interracial, the single mother found it difficult to find a man who was white, not that that issue mattered. At any rate, no one had seen her with a boyfriend other than a black one since before her daughter was born. Then along comes this fellow Jim Nance. Tall, good looks, strong chin, white. He loves the single mother, he claims, and her kids, too, both of them. They hook up, and he fits in just like good old daddy dearest. Picture perfect on top is dear old Jim, but deep down inside he's shittier than a shit hole. He's banging the little black girl soon as he moves into the house, and threatening her with bloody murder if she so much as opens her mouth. He's banging big brother too, or rather he's banging on him with anything he can get his hands on, belts, broom handles, extension cords and the like. The problem is, he tells the single mother, is that big brother has no discipline since he's been so long without a father figure in the house, and all he, good old Jim Nance, is doing is giving to him what any loving father would to his loving son. The single mother sees all this (not the banging of her daughter, just the banging on her son), and quite often it breaks her heart, but she's been so long without a man, a good white one like Jim, she's not able to make a good decision about it. She can't figure whether her son's new delinquency with the smoking and the skipping is a result of the beatings or the beatings are a result of the delinquency. So she makes another bad decision. She gets her son out of the house, sends him to live with her old parents, who live in a trailer park not too far away. She might have sent the daughter too had she not been interracial, but, well, you know how that goes. Her parents were cool with an interracial granddaughter and not cool with it at the same time, you know? And this is just what old Jim Nance had figured would go down. With big brother gone, he was free to raise little black sister in the way he saw fit and without interference. What he hadn't planned on was that a brother would love his sister the way this suspicious blond boy with the funny foot loved his, sneaking back home like that, hiding in the closet like that, watching it all go down. But like his mother, the blond kid was not known for making good decisions. Instead of keeping quiet about it until he could tell his mother or his grandparents, the thirteen-year old brother jumps out of the closet and attacks old Jim Nance. And Jim Nance beats him to death with his bare hands right there in front of his sister. Now there's a dead boy. Does Jim freak? No. He grabs the little sister by the shoulders and says to her, This is how it's gonna be with your mom, see? This is what's gonna happen to her if you tell anybody about this. It's your fault. If you hadn't come around here shaking your ass and your tits in my face like some little tramp, none of this ever would have happened. You're a whore, nothing good comes from you. You killed your brother by making me let you suck my dick. Why didn't you stop me? Why didn't you stop me? You killed your brother when you took your mama's man. Look at him. Look at how dead he is. Why did you let this happen? And now you're gonna get your mom killed too, because you don't care about anybody but yourself. You're gonna tell her what happened to your brother, and I'm gonna have to kill her and cut off her head and dig a big hole behind the trailer and dump her in it. I have no other choice. Shame on you. You're the one I should kill. You know it's the truth. You're the one because you made me love you, and I love you so much I can't kill you. I am weak. I am weak. I love you more than your mother because you're prettier than her. You are so beautiful. Look what you did to my heart. Look what you made me do to your brother. Can't you see how upset I am over this? Oh my god, I loved this boy, I only wanted what was right for him, but you, look what you made me do. Coming in here telling me how jealous you were because he was the favorite and you were black. Shame on you. Oh god, I love you. Come here. Kiss me. Sit on my lap and hold me. Look at me. Look how upset I am over this. But I'll do anything for you. I'll do anything to keep us together. But I don't want to have to kill your mom. Please don't make me have to kill your mom. Help me save your mom, okay? Don't you love your mom? Be a good girl. You have to keep our little secrets, you have to. Stop being so selfish. You should love your mom. You shouldn't make me have to cut her head off. Do you hear me? Promise me. Don't make me have to cut off your mama's head. You're the favorite one now. Here's what we're gonna do, okay? Here's what we're gonna say happened. We're gonna put his body in the lake with stones. We're gonna say a prayer over him so that he can go to heaven. I'm gonna pray, and then you're gonna pray. Then we're gonna tell everybody when they ask us that he didn't come by here today. We're gonna say we haven't seen him since the last time we visited your grandparents. Then everything is gonna be all right. He's gonna be in heaven with all good boys. And me and your mama are gonna have a baby, a boy just like him, a baby brother for you to play with. And everything is gonna be all right again. Do you hear me? Stop crying. Stop crying. Promise me. Kiss me. Now put back on your panties like a good little girl and help me get your brother down to the lake.

Fact of the matter is, the story worked. Little boys disappear every day in Miami, never to be seen again except on milk cartons or on posters hanging in the Wal-Mart express lane. Fact of the matter is, the single mother wept and wept and accused, but the police didn't have anything on Jim Nance, handsome Jim, who was surprised and hurt that he was considered a suspect after how hard he had tried to be a father to that boy, but well, that's the way it goes. No good deed goes unpunished. All of these homeless creeps and perverts walking around this city and everybody points the finger at the one decent man in town. A man who walked into this "situation" and so selflessly took care of two children (he could have said *bastards, a nigger and a gimp,* but he didn't) who were not even his own. And he kept away from the single mother for a few months, to let her see how that felt. Jim was a handsome man, and a good lover, and the police had nothing on him, and the single mother missed him, and she took him back into her home, and he promptly got her pregnant and went back to banging her black daughter behind her back. Things couldn't have been better for old Jim Nance. Except for one small problem.

It takes a killer to know a killer.

M Gantry is a killer.

She already has three notches on her gun. She cannot sleep at night because of the two who deserved to be killed, and the one who had not. She lies awake at night in her bed separating the voices in her head. The good from the evil. The words from the song. The drummer from his beat. She lies awake at night in her bed, thinking things through. Thinking about the eyes of that little girl. Such wise eyes for one so young. What does she know that she should not?

But everybody loves Jim.

Even the little girl loves Jim.

Check out Jim: His background is clean. He comes from a farm family. Upstate New York. A mediocre student, but voted friendliest in his high school graduating class. Everybody loves Jim. With his twinkly blue eyes.

A tour in the Air Force. Stationed near Thailand. Where child porn is legal. Okay. Off-topic, but interesting. Then stationed in Las Vegas, where he learned to gamble. He had been required by his superiors to join Gambler's Anonymous. Nothing wrong with that, except it didn't take. His tax records showed problems. A bankruptcy. The infamous high interest, short-term loans. Two marriages that ended in divorce after less than a year.

Talk to the ex-wives: Jim, he was a nice guy, it just didn't work out.

Everybody loves Jim.

Each ex-wife had something else in common with the single mother. Each ex-wife had a pre-teen daughter at the time she was married to Jim.

Talk to the daughters: Jim, he was a nice guy, I miss him a lot. He was a cool step dad. Everybody loves Jim.

The killer M Gantry was stunned into speechlessness. She could not believe her eyes.

Each ex-wife's former pre-teen daughter was what you might call—interracial.

Talk to the daughter:
Jim is a nice guy. I like him.
Everybody loves Jim. Has he ever hit you?

No ma'am. Oh no.

Has he ever tried anything with you?

Like what? Like that? Oh no.

Did he like your brother?

Yes, he liked him very much.

I see you do well in school.

Yes. I like school. I do all of my work.

What do you want to be when you grow up?

I want to be a doctor.

Wow. You have to get all A's to be a doctor.

I will.

It's gonna be hard.

Not for me.

A lot of kids say it's hard to get all A's. It was hard for me when I was in school.

It's easy if you do all your work. I do all my work.

Do you have a boyfriend?

Huh? Oh no. My mom doesn't let me date. I'm way too young.

Is there a boy that you like?

No.

Not one?

Not one. My mom says boys will make me mess up in school. I want to be a doctor. A foot doctor to help people with short feet like my brother.

. . . it's gonna be tough.

Not for me.

It's gonna be tough if you keep skipping school.

I don't skip school. Only fools skip school.

Your brother skipped school.

. . . *he was having problems.*

Your brother skipped school the day he disappeared.

Did he? That's what I heard.

You skipped school that day too.

(. . .)

Where did you go?

Where ma'am?

Where did you go that day you skipped school? Did you go to see your brother?

I didn't skip.

I have your records.

It's not true. I never skipped.

I went by your school yesterday. I have your records. You skipped school that day. You skip school a lot.

It's not true. I must've been sick that day.

That's what your teachers say. That you never skipped school once, but you've been sick a lot. I bet your mom doesn't know how sick you've been.

Yes, she does. She signs the note.

I could ask her.

Then ask her!

I don't have to ask her. I have a note she signed when you got the chicken pox back in third grade. Then I have all these notes from when you got sick this year. Your mom's handwriting is different on the new ones. Who signs your notes when you skip?

I don't skip. I'm telling the truth. I get sick.

Where do you go when you skip?

I'm telling the truth.

Did Jim sign your notes?

I don't know. Maybe my mom made him sign them. Maybe she was tired.

Is it okay if I ask her?

If you want! Go ahead!

Are you a virgin?

(. . .)

Did you see your brother on the day he died?

(. . .)

Did Jim see your brother on the day he died?

Can I leave now, please? I got piano lessons.

You can leave anytime you like. This is a playground. We're

just talking. None of this is official. Did you or Jim see your brother on the day he died?

I didn't see him on the day he died. I swear. And Jim didn't see him either.

Do you love Jim?

He's my stepfather. I like him a lot.

Do you love Jim?

Can I leave, please?

Do you love Jim?

(. . .)

Everybody loves Jim.

. . . everybody loves Jim.

You're not the first little girl he's done it to. Don't cry.

(. . .)

See these pictures? See? These are his other . . . step daughters.

(. . .)

All I'm saying is, how do you know Jim didn't see your brother on the day he died? Tell the truth . . . I won't tell your mom about you and Jim.

. . . you promise?

I promise.

I didn't see my brother on the day he died and Jim didn't either because me and Jim were . . . together. We don't know who killed him. Nobody does.

Then how do you know he's dead?

Huh?

You keep saying on the day he *died.*

No. You said on the day he died.

But you said it like you know it.

(. . .)

Where is your brother's body? Where did Jim put your brother's body?

He's going to kill my mom.

Where did he put your brother's body?

In the lake.

Which lake?

It wasn't his fault. He didn't know my brother was home. He didn't mean to kill him.

Which lake?

Don't hurt him.

Which lake?

Please don't let him hurt my mom.

If we find that body in the lake, he won't hurt anybody ever again. I promise you.

(. . .)

What?

He said I was sweet.

He told them all that.

Sosa shows up a half hour later, plied with coffee and aspirin, dark shades shielding his eyes from the early morning sun. His head feels swollen like a helium balloon. He pops a mint into his mouth, opens the door, puts a foot out, and spies the green sock. He checks his other foot. Black sock. He looks toward the entrance of the casino. Lambert, with his large stomach, appears there like a standing Buddha amid the crush of uniformed Seminole police officers and sheriffs deputies, and casino security guards. This is all from the commotion that M has caused.

Sosa pulls his foot back in, takes off his shoes, removes his socks, and then puts his shoes back on.

His walk is tentative as he makes his way toward Lambert, who has spotted him and is waving him over. It is like floating. He is sensitive to sound and light to the point of pain as he floats across the pavement of the parking lot. A uniformed Seminole holds up her hand, stopping him. Sosa shows his badge. The Seminole nods him through.

He hears Lambert's throaty laugh. He can see by Lambert's

overly friendly body language that he is working the Seminole police, working them hard. This is a bad sign, Sosa knows. This means that M must really have lost it. He cannot understand why Lambert calls himself her friend, then sets her up like this. Lambert knows M's temper. This should have been handled differently. The captain should have been told. Proper procedure should have been followed. Not to mention, they are out of jurisdiction. They are all going to get in serious trouble for whatever it is she has done today. Lambert must get a kick out of watching her go off on suspects this way. He has to know what it does to her. What kind of friend is he?

Sosa prays she hasn't killed the pig.

He gets to Lambert, who extends a hand, and says brightly, "And this is my other partner, Detective Sosa. M you've already met, ha-ha-ha. Sosa, this is Lt. Fireeagle. Ha-ha-ha. He understands what's going down. He's a good guy. He'll cover for us."

Sosa shakes the hand of the big, uniformed Fireeagle but says to Lambert, "Where is she?"

Lambert is all teeth and gums. Grinning. He points with his thumb at the casino entrance. "She's in there. They're taking good care of her, though. Nothing at all to worry about. Native American hospitality at its finest." He leans toward Sosa and shrieks much too loudly for Sosa's delicate ears. "So how ya feeling there, old buddy?"

"Where is she?"

"In there, I told you."

"You coming?"

Lambert winks. Whispers, "Naw, I'm kinda still talking to my friend the injun chief here—." Sosa is already pushing through the glass doors, past the ATM machines that guard the entrance, past the army of light and sound that is the casino. It does not take long to spot her. There is a bank of slot machines roped off with yellow police tape and patrolled by three burly Seminole sheriffs. She is seated on the ground with her hands cuffed behind her back. Sosa flips open his badge and the burly Seminoles let him pass under the tape. Her hair is a mess of unkempt fullness on her head. Her face is lined with rage, which begins to dissolve as soon as they catch each other's eye. Sosa gets down on the ground with her. He puts his arms around her. She leans forward, resting her weight on his shoulders as he holds her. He says into her ear: "What did you do to him?"

"A little blood. Broken nose. Pistol whip."

"Police brutality."

"I didn't get a chance to finish."

"Leave it to the system," Sosa warns. "You gotta stop taking it personal, M."

"He could get off."

"We have the body . . . he won't get off."

"There's always a chance," she says. "The girl's in love with him."

"Shit."

"Sweet he called her. Swe-e-eet."

"He got under her skin."

"He got under my skin. They always gets under my skin," she sobs. Her weight rests against his neck. She smells like the memory of perfume after a night of loving. Lambert is not the only one who has dreamt of loving M. Sosa is a happily married man, and even when he is dangerously hung over like this, he remains a man of honor. She is his partner, and nothing more than that. She says to him, "I'm still having trouble sleeping."

Sosa nods. "Shhh. Shhh," he whispers gentle against her ear.

"But I know where he is. I know where they took him."

"What are you telling me?"

"They took him through that door there." She nudges his neck with her lips in the direction of the door. Sosa knows that she means nothing by the nudging of his neck with her lips; she has no choice because her hands are cuffed. Now if her hands were not cuffed and she had touched his neck with her lips, that would have been something. She says to him, "When they opened it, I saw him cuffed to a chair. I think he's still unconscious."

"You knocked him out?"

He feels her lips smile against his neck. "I was trying to kill his ass. I wanted to beat him to death like he did that kid . . . now you'll have to do it. They'll let you in. You still have your gun."

"I won't."

"He's a pig."

"The courts'll take care of it, M. Shhh."

"Don't let him leave this place. It's what we came here for. It's what we promised." She nudges his neck. "Do it, Sosa."

"I can't. I can't. That's not me. I'm not a killer."

M pushes back and looks at him. "Like me?"

"I didn't say that."

A bank of machines nearby begins to rock, beep, and whistle loudly as a jackpot is hit. The celebratory music piping from the winning machine is tinny and repetitive, but the tune, stolen from and stripped of its original disco trappings, is familiar: *Let's dance, let's dance to the drummer's beat, Let's dance, Let's dance . . .* Somebody shouts for joy. A blue-haired old lady has hit the jackpot. She shouts again and raises her hands in the air. The other gamblers rush over to her machine to see with their own eyes what they all desire for themselves. A herd of feet and excited chatter rushes past Sosa and M.

"I didn't say that. I didn't mean that," Sosa apologizes.

But M is listening to the tinny music now. There is a strange sadness in her eyes. She lets out a groan and falls back on his neck.

"M?"

"Under my skin," she says.

"What?"

She kisses his neck. It is a kiss. One soft kiss. This has never happened before, though Sosa has dreamed. Not with this strong woman. Sosa can't understand it. "But you love me anyway, don't you?" she says groggily against his neck.

Sosa is a man of honor. Sosa is a man who loves his wife. Despite the aspirin and the coffee, he is still hung over. That will be his excuse, he decides, as he tells his partner, "Yes." He rocks her in his arms. But he is not sure whether she has heard him. "M?" he says. Rocking her gently. Rocking her sweet. "M, M, M."

She is heavy on his neck now as he holds her. He can tell by her breathing that she is asleep at last.

Gulf Stream Cox

Hibiscus Silvia Curbelo

Born under the wrong sign,
in a mess of cold stars.
The last bloom of summer.

She's counting change
at the 7-11 when he pulls up.
Old Cadillac. Salmon colored.

She buys a cherry cola and a box
of saltines. Shotgun sky, gray and long
as the ash on her next cigarette.

Sailing through what comes next.
The flame of her. Windblown.
Wide open. Moth-like in moonlight.

Rust on his spur.

Water-carrying Moon Joann Gardner

You would find him, sometimes, if not leaning over the engine
of some rusted car, then in the wedge of space behind the piano,
next to the rolled-up rugs with coffee stains, swollen hotdogs,
wires, dust.

And he would play that piano honky-tonk, with a cigarette in his mouth,
beside the broken window, so you could hear him from the road.

As the smoke would rise, he would pause and think, pulling the white
papyrus back, leaving red and ash, the whole heap aching for conflagration.

And when the golden lab-hound had puppies, we thought then
some commitment might have stirred. The first batch was dispatched
to loving homes, but later there were others, not so cute nor so robust,

and the steady trickle of loss carried them off
to the sink hole where they drowned, to the highway where they
were flattened, to the neighbor's garden where they were shot.

What more is there to say about him, except that once, before we met,
he sat outside his house and wept because his lover Claire was dead,

killed by her husband in a jealous rage because she had made love
to a white man, and that he passes on to me through the words of a friend
the name of that upturned moon I see.

Here, beyond disappointment, as he pursues his wife's sister, justifying faithlessness through some misguided mission to save.

A Conversation with Barbara Parker Barbara Mooney

Best-selling author and FIU Creative Writing Program graduate Barbara Parker has written nine successful mysteries set in South Florida. The tenth, Suspicion of Rage, *will be published in February 2005. A native of South Carolina who moved to Tampa as a teenager, she received a degree in history from the University of South Florida and a law degree from the University of Miami. She worked as a lawyer in Miami for almost ten years, first as a prosecutor in the State Attorney's office and then as a sole practitioner. At that time, writing was only a hobby. When she decided that she would rather be a full-time writer than a lawyer, she went back to school and earned a master's degree from FIU. Her master's thesis became her first successful novel,* Suspicion of Innocence *(1994). A mystery featuring Miami lawyers and lovers Gail Connor and Anthony Quintana, it initiated a series of "Suspicion" novels:* Guilt *(1995);* Deceit *(1998);* Betrayal *(1999);* Malice *(2000);* Vengeance *(2001); and* Madness *(2003).* Suspicion of Rage *(2005) will take the protagonists to Havana, Cuba. Parker has also written two stand-alone mysteries with male attorneys as protagonists:* Blood Relations *(1996) and* Criminal Justice *(1997). This hard-working writer somehow finds time to go all around the country on book tours and to writers' conferences, and has been a guest author aboard the* QE2 *on three voyages. She has a daughter who has followed in her footsteps as a lawyer, and a son who is a graphic artist. She lives in Lauderdale by the Sea with her dog, Maximilian von Mango, better known as Max.*

*   *   *

Why do you think so many contemporary mystery writers have chosen Florida, especially South Florida, as the setting for their works?

Easy. Take a look around. South Florida is never boring. It has what people in colder, grayer regions secretly wish they had: sun, sex, and intrigue. If they can't move here, at least they can open a book.

While you were writing Suspicion of Innocence, *were you already planning for it to be the first one in a series? If so, how did that affect your writing? If not, what do you now wish you had done differently?*

Innocence was planned as a stand-alone. My protagonist, a Miami lawyer, had a nine-year-old daughter—not series material. The book did so well that my editor suggested a sequel called (what else?) *Suspicion of Guilt.* After this two-book "series," I thought there was nothing left to say about these people. Besides, it was getting claustrophobic, writing from a single, female point of view (Gail Connor). I did a couple of stand-alone mysteries to clear my mind, but it's not easy to come up with new characters every time, so I went back to Gail and Anthony. The novels are now in multiple points of view, and other characters come and go, bringing their subplots with them. I don't feel boxed in.

Do I wish now that I'd done something different in laying the foundations of this series? Gail would have a bigger family. Her only sister was murdered in *Innocence.* In *Vengeance* I gave her a cousin, Jackie Bryce, a rookie cop in Stuart, Florida. I think we'll see Jackie again.

One reason for the popularity of your Suspicion *series is the sizzling cross-cultural romance between your two protagonists, Gail Connor and Anthony Quintana. In a sense, Gail, the great-granddaughter of one of the area's original settlers, represents the old Anglo Miami. Anthony, a member of an influential Cuban exile family, personifies the cosmopolitan city of today. Is their often problematic relationship, and their struggle to develop more tolerance and understanding of each other, intended to illustrate the situation in the real Miami at the present time?*

In the early 1990s, when the first book was percolating, I consciously added Quintana as a counterpoint to my WASP-y protagonist. At the time, the Anglo-Cuban divide was still deep and often painful. I moved to Miami in the mid-1970s, and my views were shaped by angry demonstrations, rock-and-bottle throwing, and vituperative rhetoric on both sides. It's not like that anymore. Gail and Anthony are just two people from different backgrounds trying to make it work.

Although Miami is a very real presence in your novels, in the two most recent ones Gail and Anthony spend most of their time in other venues. Suspicion of Vengeance *takes them north to Martin County and to the Florida State Prison at Raiford. In* Suspicion of Madness, *they travel to a private island in the Keys. What opportunities did these changes in locale offer you? Can we expect them to go even farther afield in the future?*

Since you ask . . . *Suspicion of Rage*, appearing next spring, will take them to Havana. After that, they'll probably come home to Miami. I should rent a place smack downtown to get back in touch.

Speaking of new opportunities , after your second novel, Suspicion of Guilt, *Gail and Anthony went on hiatus for a couple of years while you wrote two stand-alone mysteries, both with male protagonists: Sam Hagen, a prosecutor in the State Attorney's Miami office, in* Blood Relations, *and Dan Galindo, a former prosecutor in the U. S. attorney's office, in* Criminal Justice. *Obviously this gave you a chance to use your own experiences as a prosecutor. Why else did you decide to go in these new directions? And will Sam and/or Dan ever return?*

I created Sam Hagen and Dan Galindo to get away from Gail Connor, whose neuroses were making me crazy. She must have needed a vacation, because she's a lot more fun these days. Dan's a little too sweet for this series, don't you think? Sam would fit, but he's living in Tampa now.

How do you do male protagonists so well, especially a macho Cuban male like Anthony?

My grandmother Roxie Belle used to say, "We're all alike, we're just stitched together different." In stitching together a boy doll, I cut the pattern from real life. I watch and listen. I take notes. For inspiration I might read a "guy" novel. James Lee Burke, Scott Turow, that sort of thing.

Publishers nowadays seem to prefer that their authors stick to a successful series. Did you encounter any problems with Blood Relations *and* Criminal Justice? *Do you plan to write any more stand-alones in the future?*

Ten years ago the drive toward a series wasn't quite as strong as it is now. They let me go in a different direction because they didn't know any better. My current contract calls for two more *Suspicion* books. After that? I'm having fun with them (and the pay isn't bad), so why stop?

One theme that persists throughout your novels is the failure of the legal system to always work in the best interests of justice. For instance, in Suspicion of Vengeance, *despite all Gail's efforts a man is executed for a murder he did not commit. Her frustration with the system comes through very strongly, as does yours. How did writing this book affect your views on capital punishment?*

I went from ambivalence to about 99% opposition. (The other 1% is for people like Ted Bundy and Osama bin Laden.) The innocent have been sent to Death Row, and the guilty can be spiritually redeemed. I'll stop opposing capital punishment the day we become perfect.

Another persistent theme is the elusiveness of truth. Suspicion of Deceit, *for example, is full of deceptions, lies of both omission and commission, and conflicting interpretations of events (I love the way the story line is interwoven with rehearsals of* Don Giovanni, *an opera about one of the all-time great deceivers.) Gail is passionate in her pursuit of truth. How did your career as an attorney familiarize you with the difficulty of arriving at this goal?*

There was this small claims case where my client's new roof leaked during a storm, so we sued the roofing company. She showed me photographs of her mildewed carpet and ruined drywall. She was in tears. The roofer (a guy basically working out of his truck) said no, the day had been sunny. He had weather reports to prove it. The judge ruled for my client: "I take judicial notice of the fact that in South Florida, it can be raining on one side of the street and not the other." Somebody was lying. I still don't know who. The divorces were even murkier. Eventually it drove me nuts, and I retreated to fiction. Gail Connor is optimistic in thinking she can uncover the truth. Anthony is more of a realist.

Another theme which recurs often in your work is the intrusion of the past upon the present. In more than one novel, crimes which are committed in the present turn out to be the results of, or responses to, events which took place many years ago. You were a history major for part of your undergraduate career at the University of South Florida. Did this interest in the past and its effects carry over into your fiction?

For me, history was always a *story*. Every political conflict presents a mystery: "How did this happen?" "Whose version can we believe?" There aren't many works of fiction that were not inspired by some event in the past, from action thrillers (*The Iliad, Moby Dick*) to domestic drama (*Antigone, Ethan Frome*).

Before you switched to history, you were a drama major. How has this influenced your approach to writing?

If not for my brief but intense involvement in the drama department at the University of South Florida, I doubt that I would have become a writer. Taking on a role or directing a play or scene requires the close study of character, language, and dramatic structure. What events can motivate a mother (Medea) to kill her children? Why is this fading Southern beauty (Blanche Dubois) going slowly insane? How can we keep the audience from nodding off during this monologue? What punch can we add to Act Two?

When you decided to make another switch, from lawyer to author, you enrolled in the creative writing program at FIU. How did this experience help you to become a successful writer?

I might have continued to write, but not as well. The FIU writing program provided three major boosts to my career: structure, inspiration, and contacts. I learned what a story is. (You think you know, but it's not that simple.) I was inspired by reading truly great writers, the beacons of literature. And I made friends who have helped me along the way. I don't know about other professions, but writers are a fairly nice bunch.

You have published nine books in the past ten years, and a tenth one is coming out early in 2005. Judging by the number of sources in your "Acknowledgements" you do a great deal of research for each one. You must have excellent work habits. How do you find the time for all of this? Can you tell us something about your methods?

That's not so many. Nora Roberts has written . . . what, five hundred? But she's from outer space. Most writers are like me: We plod. Most of our time is spent trying to figure out what the story is. Another chunk of time is used up pushing words around the computer screen. And then there's the research. That's the fun part. You get to talk to people doing jobs you wish you had or jobs you didn't know existed. I've talked to ballerinas, models, doctors, undercover cops, boat builders. Right now I'm trying to get in touch with a guy in Texas who can tell me how radioactive materials are used in copper mining. How do I find time for all this? It's my job. I show up for work like everybody else.

You also seem to find time to make public appearances on book tours and at writer's conferences, and have been a guest author aboard the QE2 *on three voyages. What do these obligations entail, and how much do you enjoy them?*

Yes, it was so terribly difficult to fit a three-week Pacific cruise from Sydney to Hong Kong into my schedule! They made me do three lectures! I barely had a chance to go to the spa or snooze in my deck chair. Seriously though, I can't complain, even when I'm chained to my computer trying to make a deadline. The best part of being a writer is hearing people say your book meant something to them. This is like a food pellet to a lab rat. You just have to go back and hit the levers again.

How far ahead do you plan when you begin a book? If you outline, how closely can you stick to it, or do your characters tend to take over at some point?

I used to work almost entirely from an outline. I needed the net, a safety harness, and a spotter. I still have an outline, but it's more of a general idea. Writing Chapter Four, I don't need to know what's in Chapter Thirty. After ten books (and a couple we don't need to talk about) I trust that the other trapeze will be there when I let go. My characters don't "take over." I'm the boss . . . but sometimes they creep into my study at night and leave sticky notes on the computer screen.

What writers have influenced you as an author? Which ones do you read for pleasure?

The list would go on and on and on...I'll give you three names that come to mind. Raymond Carver, P.D. James, Arthur Koestler.

Focus, motivation, conscience. The last book I read for pure pleasure was *The DaVinci Code*. To my horror, I couldn't put it down.

What advice do you have for aspiring authors?

You know that a good answer to this question could fill several books (and has). A short answer is likely to be "Never give up," which I don't like as much as Martin Cruz Smith's advice: "Quit if you can." Hemingway put it simply too: He said to write as well as you can and finish what you start.

Here's my advice: Starting out, write like you talk. (This is a variation on "Find your voice.") The big problem I notice in beginning writers' manuscripts is that they sound so phony. Maybe they're afraid to grub around in the dirt. Try this: Have your character write a letter explaining what's going on in his life. Be as profane, as shallow and selfish, as needy as you can be. Don't hold back. Nobody's going to read it. Just put the words on the page and see where they take you.

It would be great to have Raymond Chandler's steel nerves: " . . . when I split an infinitive, God damn it, I split it so it will stay split, and when I interrupt the velvety smoothness of my more or less literate syntax with a few sudden words of barroom vernacular, that is done with the eyes wide open and the mind relaxed but attentive. This method may not be perfect, but it is all I have."

All Earthly Hues David Kirby

> The sweet tinges of sunset skies and woods; yea,
> and the gilded velvets of butterflies, and the but-
> terfly cheeks of young girls. . .
>
> — *Moby-Dick*, Chapter 44 ("The Whiteness of the Whale")

I'm at the funeral of sweet, much-loved old man Ivan Johnson
    at the little antebellum church on Park Avenue,
and Dr. Johnson was so adored that there's no room
    downstairs, so I end up in the "slave gallery,"
and as I look down and wait for the service to begin,

I notice that everyone downstairs has a hymnal,
    but not we children of Paradise. Reason: there are no hymnals
upstairs because there are no hymnal *racks* upstairs,
    since slaves weren't literate. So if I had a hymnal,
I'd have to set it down on the rail, and when I got up,

I might knock it off and crack the head
    of some godly planter: "Oh, lord, I've gone and busted
Squire Carter right in the middle of that big old head
    of his! How I wish he'd have let Miss Lily go on
with those reading lessons—then I'd have had that book

in my hands and not placed it athwart that confounded rail
    and thus occasioned this sad fortuity!"
About this time, the minister, by all outward
    appearances a man of industry, frugality, and sobriety,
begins to shout like a truck-route snakehandler!

Small wonder: even the Catholic Church of my youth,

with its bedizened clergy and Latinate ritual,
has become a shabby, colloquial affair, its sonoroties anglicized
        and drawled by a padre dressed more like a camp chaplain
than a duly-anointed representative of His Holiness,

The Pope, himself still multilingual and nattily attired,
    if, for my taste, a bit too unbending on the matter
of birth control. To wit, this reporter has covered this story before,
        and whereas, as a 14 year-old
listening to Father Grifasi at St. Aloysius, I used to plot

military takeovers, calculating how many men I'd need
    and what kind of arms they'd require
to empty the church and send everyone packing,
        now, considerably older and more peaceable,
I find myself thinking, as Pastor Bob natters on,

of three guys with whom I'd had more or less acquaintance
    over the years, first guy being a magician
who was famous for saying that magicians can't play cards,
        because if they win, they look like cheaters,
and if they lose, they look like lousy magicians.

Second guy, named Albert Camous, is a Frenchman
    who was born in Algeria just before World War I
and who moved to France and made a career in business,
        and once he was walking down
a Paris street when whom should he run into

but a school chum from his North African days
    who says, "Oh, but Albert, how proud we are,
zuh uzzer boys and I, to 'ave 'ad such a
        distinguished playmate, zuh author of
L'Etranger and *La Chute* and now zuh winner

of zuh *Prix Nobel*," and I could see where this was going,
    I mean, I started to get physically ill
as his story approached an ending as inevitable
        as a car wreck, so to get it over with
as quickly as possible, I put my hand on his arm and said,

"Please don't tell me you told your chum
    you were Albert Camous the businessman
and not Albert Camus the novelist," and Albert Camous
        the businessman looked at me with Gallic
sang-froid and said, "But, of course. Why I would lie to heem?"

He'd broken the heart of his friend and probably missed out
    on an opportunity for a really good free meal,
and all in the name of *la verité*. Third guy's a little kid,
        a pal of mine who called his toothbrush
his "meenter-meinter," and everyone in his family

thought it was so cute they called their toothbrushes
    meenter-meinters, too, and it wasn't until
he went to camp and told one of the other boys that he had
        a really swell-looking meenter-meinter
that he realized what a disservice his adoring parents and siblings

had done him. His name was John Mathis and he's now
    John Mathis the public utility lawyer in California
and not Johnny Mathis the singer,
        whose "Twelfth of Never" is still played
instead of "The Wedding March" by numerous church organists

who can't persuade strong-willed brides otherwise.
    And by the way, reader, that "Wedding March"

was composed by the guy known as Felix Mendelssohn
　　　to us but as Felix Mendelssohn-Bartholdy
to his mother, Mrs. Bartholdy! My, how the years get away

from one. First time I read Hawthorne, I thought he was anxious
　　　and unhappy: then I realized *I* was! 30 years later,
he seems all bold and brave, all full of purpose
　　　and new ideas, all set to put "the rusty iron frame-work
of society"out by the curb so the Solid Waste Management boys

can heave it on their truck while he and Emerson and Thoreau
　　　and even Melville, clearly brimming with genius
yet a bit too puppyish in his devotion to a man of whom
　　　his own wife said, "Hawthorne hates to be touched
more than any other person I know," knock together

their big utopian America of smart, busty women
　　　and broad-shouldered guys who raise their own vegetables
and churn their own butter and cobble their own shoes
　　　and free the slaves *and* give Texas back to the Mexicans.
So Hawthorne was right then and he's right now,

and he didn't change a word! Go figure, you epistemologists!
　　　Oh, *la verité, la verité*—
what in the whole ass-biting *qu'est-ce que c'est*
　　　is *la verité* in the first place?
According to C. S. Lewis, there weren't enough

dons to grade the lit exams at Oxford
　　　during the second World War, so one of the faculty
from History was brought in, and he began grading
　　　quietly enough, but soon he was snorting
with indignation, and after the fifth or sixth exam paper, he said,

"I say, Lewis, your chaps seem to think
      that if something sounds good, it must be true!"
Or you could put it this way: both"We Shall Overcome"
            and "A Change Is Going to Come"
deal with the same subject, so why is the former

more popular, even though the latter
      is a better song? My analysis: "We Shall Overcome"
is easier to memorize because it's repetitive
            and doesn't have any images in it.
Images are the thing, aren't they, reader? Quite the little dealmaker,

those images: when Sam Cooke sings he was born
      by a river in a little tent, you, who were born in
a hospital in Sheboygan or Eau Claire, say,
            I was born by the river! *I*, too, was born in a little tent,
just as Our Savior was born in a manger in a baking desert,

in a country so dry they didn't even have the word "river"
      in the dictionary! They probably didn't even have dictionaries!
Or if they did, somebody'd say "Look up a word,"
            and somebody else'd say, "Can't! Too hot!"
Winding down from a great I-saw-the-light hullaballoo

about all the sanctified hubba-bubbas
      waiting upstairs for us under God's big sun,
Pastor Bob announces that dapper old man Ivan Johnson
            is in Heaven at this very moment, which I'd say
is a world-class no-brainer, for if there are only two choices,

suffice it to say that Dr. Johnson's not going to end up
      in the Hot Place shoveling brimstone under the supervision
of some sarcastic imp or archfiend. But so it goes in the land
            of the bichromatic, where every act, word, wish, choice,

and aspiration is as white as Squire Carter's big ol' butt cheeks,

as black as the soil of Mother Africa. What about your grays,
      though, your drabs, your duns, not to mention
your Land's End or J. Crew catalog colors, your fawn, taupe,
            quartz,plum, camel? Poor lost Vincent Van Gogh
had this yarn ball made up of strands of different-colored wools

that he would place next to each other until he found
      just the right combination, your red next to your indigo,
your orange between your cerise and your violet but not too close
            to your crimson, your blue, until he said
That's it, that's a world worth living in, that's the one for me.

Monkey's Fist Christine Kling

They had been married twenty-two years when he came home early one afternoon and announced he had bought himself a boat. She sat at the kitchen table grading papers, and she looked up at him, trying to break her focus away from Reynaldo's interpretation of Crane's "The Open Boat."

"What did you say?" She thought she hadn't heard him right, had somehow confused his spoken words with Reynaldo's written words. He'd probably bought himself a new coat.

He lifted her heavy gray braid and kissed her on the back of the neck. "It's an Irwin fifty-seven. I know that's pretty big for a first boat, but I wanted something we would be comfortable on when we go to the Bahamas." He slipped off the wind breaker with the company name stenciled across the back and draped it over an empty chair. "No crappy little shower in the head or doing without air. And ice, gotta have ice. This boat's got it all. Tons of electronics, radar, GPS, chart plotter. A ten KW generator, nice big Ford Lehman diesel. Ketch-rigged, too," he said. He'd been staring out the windows as he'd listed the boat's amenities, but now he glanced down at her for a brief moment. "That means it has two masts, honey."

"Right," she said.

He dropped his briefcase on the kitchen counter, and he took a highball glass out of the dishwasher, filled it with ice at the refrigerator door and walked into the living room, headed for the bar cabinet and his bourbon. She heard the sound of the television as he clicked it on, and she knew he would be sitting in there in his chair with the television blaring - and reading.

He'd started buying sailing books about a year earlier. First, there were the adventure tales of couples who had crossed the oceans and cruised the South Seas. He stacked those on the end table next to his Barcalounger. Then he got into the how-tos, and lately she noticed he had purchased a cruising guide to the Bahamas.

She kept her books shelved neatly by subject with separate sections for poetry, novels, short story collections or anthologies, and critical works. He had reshelved her poetry, stacking the slender paperbacks on top of her Oxford English Dictionary and Riverside Shakespeare to make room for his sailing books. He now had enough to require a shelf of his own.

She bent her head over the stack of essays from her eleventh-grade AP English students and went back to work. After deciding Reynaldo was parroting someone else's thoughts, she gave him a C and moved on. The kitchen table was her favorite spot to work; the light was good, thanks to the corner windows that overlooked the backyard, the pool and the canal beyond. She could get away without having to wear those damn reading glasses as long as the light was good enough. She could also watch the birds from here, the blue jays and mockingbirds who frequented the feeder she'd hung in the old oak, the only tree he'd saved on the lot.

They'd moved in about five years ago when he had finally started doing really well and branched out on his own, building spec houses and small groups of townhouses. She often missed the simple, cinder block, two-bedroom home with a white barrel tile roof they'd sold for almost three times what they'd paid for it. She had invested time there in painting bookshelves, polishing terrazzo and potting orchids, and she'd reaped the good memories of their early years together.

What had happened to real estate values in South Florida in the same time period was practically obscene, and no matter how ugly or opulent the homes he built seemed to her, there were always more nouveau riche types who could not wait to have him tear down the little fifty-year old cottages here in Victoria Park or over in Rio Vista so he could build them another McMansion. This lot where they now lived had been unusually small, and he'd decided after the spec house had been on the market for six months, that rather than take a beating on the price, they would move in and call it their home. After all, as the president and owner of a construction company in Fort Lauderdale, he deserved a classy address, a nice place to entertain clients, he'd told her.

At dinner that night, he chewed a large forkful of her chicken and rice and announced, "You're gonna have to learn how to sail." Little bits of rice escaped and flew out of his mouth. They landed back on his plate.

She nodded at that.

"It'll be a tight fit," he said, "but we're going to bring the boat up to the dock here at the house. She's over at Bahia Mar right now. I told the broker I'd have her out of there by Saturday. That gives us about a month to get ready. I invited Gator and his wife to go with us to Nassau next month - when you're off on Spring Break. Should be a nice way to break in the boat."

Gator was his best friend from high school who had made a fortune in the dot com glory days and had been smart enough to get out before the bubble burst. He'd recently married for the third time.

"What's her name?"

"Gator's wife?"

"No, your boat."

"She's called the *Verity*. Don't know if I like that, especially because it's in some foreign language, but I hear it's bad luck to change a boat's name."

"Verity means truth."

"I *know* that."

Saturday morning he told her they would take her Lexus to the marina, bring the boat to the house, and then they'd go back to get her car. When they walked into the broker's office, a thin white-haired man got up from behind his desk, buttoning his blazer and putting on his smile. "You must be the missus," he said in a pronounced British accent. She couldn't believe he had really called her that. "Congratulations. It's a lovely boat." His breath smelled of stale cigarettes.

It was quite clear her husband wanted to get rid of the broker as soon as possible. From the moment the man had suggested that they might want to hire a captain to help them the motor to their dock, her husband had shut down. He wanted the broker off his boat. It didn't happen too often anymore, but her husband could be rude when he wanted to be.

With the broker gone, he had taken her on a tour down below. She was surprised by the amount of space and all the comforts that had been squeezed into that compact environment. It reminded her of a dollhouse. He showed her the galley first with the electric stove and the top-loading refrigerator and freezer. When she lifted the lid of the freezer, the dark hole smelled musty. She would need to do lots of cleaning, she thought, and wondered when she would find the time.

The aft cabin would be theirs, he said as he opened the small round door and stepped through.

She poked her head past his shoulder and remarked that the queen-sized bed nearly took up all the space in the cabin.

"It's called a berth, honey."

Back on deck he began to explain to her about directions on the boat, fore and aft, port and starboard. The dock they were tied to was shaped like the letter T and they were tied at the end. It looked as though it would be quite easy to motor out, she thought. Just untie the ropes and off they would go. He explained to her over and over what he would do, and what he expected her to do. He took her up onto the front of the boat and picked up a white rope with a small, knotted rope ball on the end. This rope looked newer than the others on the boat.

"This is called a heaving line," he said. "I was surprised they didn't have one on the boat. According to *The Marlinspike Sailor*, it's a necessity. See, on this end?" He held up the knotted ball. "This is called a monkey's fist. The weight of it makes it easier to throw the line."

It was almost more square than round, and she liked the look of it. Decorative, that's what she'd call it. She'd seen jewelry in that shape before, little gold versions that sold for hundreds of dollars in the shops on Las Olas.

"When we get up to the house, Gator's gonna be there. I asked him to come over to help us dock." He held the coiled rope in one hand and swung the loose end with the monkey's fist. "You're gonna take this line and when we get to within about ten feet of the dock you're gonna throw this to Gator like this." He tossed the monkey's fist back at the mast and released the coils he held in his left hand. The rope arced up through the air and landed past the mast on the plastic windshield of the boat. "You've always got to remember to let go of the line in this hand, see," he held up his left hand, "or the fist end isn't gonna go but about five feet and fall in the water. Okay, you try it."

He coiled up the line, stood behind her and placed the coils in her left hand, the throwing end in her right. "Now swing this end back like this," he said and pulled her right hand back, " then swing forward and let go."

She released the rope and the fist flew about ten feet and landed at the base of the mast. The coils dropped at her feet a second later.

"All right. That's good enough, honey. You keep practicing."

Gator was standing on their seawall, waving as they rounded the corner into the canal. Her husband was wearing his cell phone on his belt with a black wire that snaked up into his ear. He'd kept a running dialogue going with his friend throughout the trip from the marina.

"Okay, you ready up there, honey? Don't throw it until I say when, okay?" He was shouting so loud, she looked around to see if any of their neighbors were outside. All the windows were closed tight to keep the cold air inside, and the only people she saw were the gardeners in front of her neighbor's cottage.

It wasn't difficult to see which home was theirs. It was the only two-story house built out to within what seemed like inches of the property line on either side. The home was painted gray with a silvery tin roof and an imitation widow's walk. It would have looked more at home in New England than South Florida.

She glanced back at him standing in the cockpit. She thought the boat seemed to be going too fast. His hands gripped the massive stainless steel wheel at two o'clock and ten o'clock. His legs were braced shoulder length apart. He was not a large man, and the size of the steering wheel made him appear even smaller. Ahead, their dock was coming up fast. She passed the monkey's fist into the hand holding the coiled line and shaded her eyes looking back at him.

"Get ready, honey. You ready?"

She heard a change in the sound of the engine. It revved louder, and she decided he had shifted into reverse. The boat speed slowed only slightly and the back of the boat began to twist away from the dock pointing the bow toward the seawall beyond their wood dock.

"What the hell are you doing? Throw Gator the line, goddamn it!"

She swung the fist back and threw, and the white rope flew nearly straight up, then dropped down only inches from the dock. Gator cartwheeled his arms, trying to grab the line before it splashed into the water. He missed.

Her husband pushed her aside, ran forward, and pushed the boat off the dark wood piling with his shoulder. The sound of wood, fiberglass and metal crunching together as the tons of boat rammed the dock made her smile.

Later, he assured her it wasn't *all* her fault, and besides, there wasn't really all that much damage to the boat. It was mostly cosmetic, just some scratches in the fiberglass, and he could easily get the kinks taken out of that stainless steel railing on the bow. His *Verity* could take a beating, he said. He'd known she'd be a strong, sound boat.

"You're just gonna need to spend some time practicing before we take off for the Bahamas. It'll be good for you. Get you back in shape. And I'll teach you everything you need to know."

She had met him when she had taken a job as a secretary at the construction company when she'd finally decided it was time to get serious about finishing her college degree. She was twenty-eight years old, and she had been dropping in and out of college for almost ten years. Her parents kept insisting that she simply needed to lose a few pounds, and then she'd finally get married and wouldn't have to worry about school anymore. The project was a condominium complex down on the beach, and he was the foreman on the job. They'd dated less than a year before they got married, but she often wondered if it was the fact that they'd dated less than a week before she slept with him that had made him stop listening to her so early in their marriage. His face was badly scarred from teenage acne and his rounded shoulders did little to increase his small stature. Perhaps he figured that a girl who would sleep with him so quickly couldn't be all that bright.

Teaching surprised her. She had always been a bookworm as a kid, and she found that sharing this love of books with class-rooms full of reluctant teenagers satisfied her in a way that nothing else ever had. And she was good at it. She was not a strong and assertive teacher, but her students admired her quiet nature. She could not remember how many times through the years she had heard one of her students yell at another to "Shut up and let the lady talk." And they listened to her. They cared about what she had to say.

*   *   *

Gator and Cindy, his new wife, came over for dinner the night before they were to leave for their week in the Bahamas. The young woman could not have been more than thirty years old, and she was wearing a pink tank top with a push-up bra that reminded her of the waitresses in Hooters, one of her husband's favorite lunch spots.

"I've never been sailing before," Cindy gushed when she came into the kitchen and offered to help. "Gator says that if we like it, we're gonna get ourselves a boat even bigger than yours."

"That would be nice," she said and handed Cindy a large wooden salad bowl heaped high with greens to take out to the dining room.

She was tired. Her students had been wild the day before spring break, bursting with energy and not the least bit willing to discuss Zora Neale Hurston. She had thought that the scenes of the hurricane's devastation would touch these Florida kids, but they were all too young to remember Andrew, the last hurricane to hit the area. All her time outside school lately had been spent getting the boat ready for their trip and practicing with the heaving line as her husband had told her to do.

After dinner, her husband took Gator and Cindy out to the boat to show them around, teach them how to use the marine head and to help them settle their bags in their cabin. There were two guest cabins forward with double berths and her husband laughed loudly and winked when he told Gator that there wasn't much room up there in those berths, that it was a good thing he had a skinny wife.

She was glad when they'd gone out the back door, glad when she clicked off the stereo and the house grew quiet. She almost thought she could begin to like this house, if only it could be quiet more often. When she had finished loading the dishwasher, she pulled the full bag out of the plastic bin under the sink and tied the red ties in a neat bow. She opened the back door and stepped around to put the bag in the can on the side of the house. When she came back around the house, she saw the three of them standing on the pool deck, pausing to talk in lowered voices before going back into the house. Her hand paused on the doorknob and she stepped back into the shadows of the narrow passage between their house and the wood fence along the property line.

Cindy reached for the sliding glass door. "I've got to go to the little girl's room. See you inside."

The two men watched her go in. Her husband shook his head.

"Gator, I don't know how you do it. What I wouldn't give for something like that."

"You just say the word, brother man. Cindy's friend, Kiki, she's gonna be staying over on Paradise Island. She would love to go sailing with us. With you."

"You don't know how much I'd like that, too," her husband said. "The thing is, I know she'll hate it." He jerked his head toward the house. "Sailing. Especially if it's rough. I'm pretty sure that by the time we get to Nassau, it would be easy enough to convince her to hop a plane for home."

"Then it's a plan."

"I don't know," he said.

"Man, I don't get you," Gator said. "You could have your pick of women. That one," he said and nodded toward the French doors that led into the kitchen. "Look at her." He spread his hands wide. "And she didn't say a word all through dinner. Why the hell do you stay married to her?"

"What? Gator, how can you ask me that after what your exes have taken from you? I'll take the monkey on my back before I'll give her half of what's mine."

The next morning they were motoring out through Port Everglades Channel when the gray light in the east started to turn pink and soon the gray wooly clouds were tinged with crimson.

She came up the ladder balancing two mugs of hot coffee wearing her sweats to ward off the March chill air. Her husband was stowing the last of the dock lines in the cockpit locker under the seat. She handed him a steaming mug and turned to look at the spectacle in the east.

"You know what they say," she said to no one in particular. Gator and Cindy had shown up wearing shorts and tank tops, and they were cuddling under a blanket in the back of the cockpit. "Red sky at night, sailor's delight. Red sky at morning, sailor take warning."

Her husband squinted ahead. "Where'd you pick that up?"

"Read it in one of your books," she said.

He laughed. "Ran out of your own books? Yeah, well, cold front came through overnight, but it should be clearing up later." He took a sip of the hot coffee. "Think you can handle a little rough weather, honey?"

She shrugged. "Are you sure it's wise to go if we know the weather's going to be bad?" The bow plunged into the first of the seas and spray splattered across the deck, peppering the clear plastic windows across the front of the cockpit.

"Damn," he said when the deck seemed to drop out from under them in the next trough, and he spilled his coffee down the front of his Dockers. "Clean that up, will you?"

She struggled down the ladder and grabbed a dishtowel hanging on the front of the stove. As she mopped up the brown liquid, more seawater splashed aboard. "Don't you think it would be wiser to turn back?" she asked. "Wait a few days for this weather to settle down?"

"Honey, this boat can take it. Should take us about thirty hours to get to Nassau. We'll get in late tomorrow morning. The *Verity* can take whatever nature can dish up."

Gator took over the wheel while her husband got the sails set. The *Verity* had roller furling and electric winches, so the men were able to unfurl the sails without leaving the shelter of the cockpit. She watched them push buttons to pull the sails out, and wondered that this is what sailing had come to now. Gator had to let go of the wheel twice to heave over the side. Her husband teased him about the amount of beer he'd drunk the night before, but his friend wasn't laughing when he hunched back under the blanket with his new wife. Cindy's eyes had great dark circles under them where the salt spray has caused her mascara to run, and she was soaked through, her teeth chattering. Gator groaned and dry heaved a couple more times, then mumbled that he was going below and disappeared down the ladder with Cindy right behind him.

The sails steadied the motion of the boat somewhat, and made the seas appear less frightening. Her husband set the boat to run on autopilot and went below to change out of his wet clothes and put on his foul weather gear. He told her to call him if she saw any other boats or ships.

It was as though they owned the sea that day. There were no other boats or ships as far as she could see in any direction. She was surprised at how quickly the buildings of Fort Lauderdale were shrinking off their stern. They would soon be surrounded by nothing but gray angry water. Occasionally, one of the seas broke at its peak and made a rushing noise like a wheezy monster exhaling, and when one of those breaking seas hit them, the autopilot groaned and ground its gears in protest as it attempted to right their course.

She heard her husband rummaging around in the galley below, opening the refrigerator, clanking pottery. He stepped a few steps up the ladder and threw an empty quart milk carton over the side. She stared open-mouthed, startled by the flagrant littering.

"It can handle a milk carton," he said. "It's a big ocean."

She turned away from him and watched the white carton rise up on the face of a swell and disappear into the next trough. She saw the white flash only one more time on the peak of a swell before it was lost in the sea of gray. In less than a minute, it was gone.

When her husband came back up the ladder, he was out-fitted from top to bottom in a yellow plastic suit. On his feet, he wore shiny new black sea boots. He settled on the cockpit seat and looked around the horizon. A few minutes later he checked the sails, then he checked his watch.

"Only about twenty-eight more hours to go," he said.

By late morning the seas had grown worse. The boat was heeled over at a constant twenty-degree angle. She tried going below, but she felt the nausea begin, so she grabbed a paperback novel and found she could read tucked up under the canvas shelter he called a dodger. There, most of the spray missed her. When noon came around, none of them felt like eating, and the only time she saw Cindy was when she came out to fetch the plastic trash can from the galley to use as a puke bucket in their cabin.

Her husband went up and down the ladder all afternoon. The boredom of sailing was something he had not reckoned with. He played with the radio below trying to raise other vessels, then came out into the cockpit and pushed buttons on the electric winches, taking in lines and letting them out again. She'd read over two hundred pages of the espionage thriller, but she was having a difficult time following the plot. The boat was groaning and below, whenever they rose on an extra large swell, the contents of the cabinets rattled and shook. She imagined broken catsup bottles and spilled vinegar. The *Verity* was a very high-sided boat, but when the wires on the low side started dipping underwater as the stronger gusts hit them, she decided she should say something.

"Don't you think we have too much sail up? Surely we're going fast enough." She'd read enough in those books of his to know that when the wind got stronger, you were supposed to put up smaller sails or take them in altogether.

A blast of spray hit the dodger, and it sounded like a round of BB's hitting the plastic window. Her husband had his yellow hood cinched tight around his pinched face. "This boat can take it, honey, don't you worry. Why don't you go down and fix me something hot to eat."

She looked at her watch and was surprised to see it was after five. It would be getting dark soon with the gloom of the heavy overcast and the patch of even darker clouds on the horizon ahead. They hadn't seen much rain this day, but judging from the look of those black clouds, they would shortly. The sun, though they wouldn't see it, would set just before six. She tucked a bookmark in her novel and made her way down the ladder holding tight and determined to keep the nausea at bay.

She decided a can of Campbell's Chunky Soup was the best she could do, and by the time she'd found a can opener and emptied the brown muck into the pot on the gimbaled stove, she was nearly sick. She braced herself on the seat of the navigation table as the cabin grew darker and the soup did its best to prove the adage about a watched pot. She cut off a thick slice of sourdough bread and a chunk of cheddar cheese, wrapped them in a paper towel, and tucked them into her sweatshirt pocket. She poured the soup into a large bowl and made her way to the ladder. The motion was even worse and the degree of heel had increased. She had to walk on the side of the ladder, and she knew she was going to spill the soup. He would be furious.

She'd just made it to the top of the ladder and was reaching out trying to pass him the bowl of soup when he said, "Canned soup? Is that the best you can do?" Then the boat shuddered from the pounding of a huge wave, and she started to go over. She saw his face turn up, away from her, and in the next second a wall of green water dropped from the sky and enveloped him. Gallons poured down the hatch bowing her head under the force of it, nearly knocking her off the ladder. The soup bowl was gone from her hand, and she wasn't even aware of having dropped it, only that she was holding on with both hands as the boat went completely over on her side. She was choking, gagging and spitting up salt water, and, when she raised her head, he was gone.

She scrambled into the cockpit as the boat righted herself and looked off the low side of the boat. She turned, looking forward and aft and saw no splash of yellow. The lifelines were still intact, but he was gone.

"Man overboard!" she hollered as loud as she could. "Man overboard!"

She hit at the buttons that should wind up the sails and looked up to see the mainsail gone, some fuzzy tatters blowing in the wind. She reached down and tried to remember the steps he'd taken when he'd started the engine. She pushed the heater and counted to ten as Gator's colorless face appeared in the companionway.

"What happened?"

She pointed over her shoulder. "He's back there somewhere. Got to start the engine."

Gator called over his shoulder. "Cindy, get on the radio and start calling mayday. Try to raise the Coast Guard."

He climbed out just as the diesel roared to life. She lifted the cockpit locker and grabbed the heaving line. "Circle around this way," she said. "Look for his yellow jacket."

Clutching the line, she crawled forward slowly, moving from handhold to handhold, keeping her body low to the deck, her heart pounding and her teeth chattering as much from the cold as from fear. She was surprised that she did not feel particularly frightened. The waves were still huge, but they'd turned the boat side on to them now, and she was rolling from one side to the other, the mast swinging in a wide arc through the black sky. She squinted into misty darkness, scanning the sea slowly, remembering the milk carton, giving him time to rise between the troughs. What she did feel was anger. Why hadn't he listened to her?

It was Cindy who spotted him. "Over there," she cried. "See him? Over there."

She thought she saw a speck of yellow, then it was gone.

Night was on them. Gator was turning the boat back into the wind. The spray stung her cheeks and burned her eyes. There. She thought she saw something yellow. She arranged the coils of the heaving line in her left hand and transferred the monkey's fist to her right, swinging the weight of it comfortably off her hand.

"I don't want to get too close. I'm afraid I'll run him down," Gator yelled into the wind. "Do you see him?" He was running from one side of the cockpit to the other, his voice high-pitched with panic. "Can you see him?"

One minute she couldn't find him anywhere, and then he was there, about twenty feet downwind, and they were going to pass him moving at a pretty good speed. She swung the fist back and shouted at him, "Here!" Just before she let go, she saw his face, saw his lips moving. He was talking – he wasn't listening to her. She let the monkey's fist fly, and a fraction of a second later, she released the coils in her left hand. The line fell short, splashed into the sea. As they steamed on past the yellow dot bobbing in the trough, she felt the corner of her lip twitch.

"Goddamn it!" Gator yelled. "I'll come around again. Cindy, try to keep your eyes on him."

"Where is he?" Cindy shouted. She raced to the stern and threw the yellow horseshoe life preserver into the night. It skittered across the surface as the wind caught it, then it disappeared in a trough.

A strong gust caught the headsail and Gator fought to bring the boat around. When they came around again Gator kept screaming, "Can you see him? He's got to be here. Can you see him out there?"

The Coast Guard told them via radio to keep circling in the area, to keep searching. Cindy and Gator clutched each other wrapped in a blanket, standing at the helm as they circled round and round. Occasionally, Cindy ducked below to read their position off the GPS for the Coast Guard radioman. The two of them were cried out by the time a Coast Guard Cutter reached them four hours later.

Her eyes were red too, more from the salt sting of squinting into the misty night. After an hour on deck, she had retreated to the corner of the cockpit where she sat huddled under the dodger staring into the blackness. When the cutter appeared at last, they launched a fast black inflatable speedboat with four men aboard wearing orange rainsuits. She climbed out of the cockpit, still clutching the heaving line. Their boat was about twenty feet off when she let fly the monkey's fist, and it landed squarely in the hands of the yeoman in the bow of the boat.

"Nice shot," Cindy said.

"Yeah," she said. "I've been practicing."

Murder Abigail Purdy

I open my mouth,
but only her scream comes out.
I try to make it stop
and her soft neck
is like the pond at my friend Billy's house
where we swam as children.
There was a small fountain in the center
where we'd find the fish.
If I was really fast, I could grab one
and squeeze it between my hands,
feel the fish parts glide against each other
under the slick skin under my fingers
which didn't even fit the whole way round.
Billy dog-paddled and stared
as I neatly tread and held the slippery thing,
the light scrape of the tail against the glow
of my chest, whitegreen beneath pondwater.
I brought it up to the surface and watched
the unmoving suspicious eyes, watched the widely
delicate mouth press against the air, breathing
and dying at the same time.

Aura Abigail Purdy

At five, we laid down
on large strips of butcher paper,
arms and legs spread,
while someone stood over us
with a black crayon
and traced our outline.
Standing up, we'd look down
at a vision of ourselves,
knobby and imperfect,
without edges or end.

I trudged home from the bus stop,
dragging my butcher paper
shadow behind me, anxious
to show my mother.
But I was locked out again,
the house was dark,
and the wooden planks
on the porch were cold.
Two hours later, my mother lifted me
in her strong arms and carried me
from my curl on the doormat
to the couch.

"I'm sorry, baby. Mrs. Binn
kept me late doing laundry."
And as my shadow bounced
away on the breeze, my eyes
burned with a closed fury.

In the twenty years since,

I have seen Mrs. Binn
in the faces of the women
at the supermarket,
at the pharmacy,
looking back at me
from the church pews.

She apologizes now.
For the way she worked
my mother till death,
wrinkled her hands
with bleaches and cleansers,
apologized for the doormat,
for my mother's long walks from the bus
in the dark. ˙She apologizes with wide
eyes, gasping apologies, with her stockings
wound around her neck,
stockings rinsed by a woman
she never cared about, mother
to a son softly sucking his thumb
on Welcome.

Gulf Stream Cox

In the Men's Group
of the Twenty-First Century Sterling Watson

"How to be a man in the twenty-first century? That's the question up for grabs tonight, guys. Who wants to start?"

The leader was an assistant pastor who'd told them he had a master's degree in family counseling, and he was, well, a man. Those were his qualifications. He smiled, waited.

Lee Turner, forty and recently separated from his wife, had arrived late on purpose and found a seat in the back row. He was happy with his place, thought not particularly with his life at the moment. He had come here tonight because his wife had suggested it during one of the despairing discussions of his inadequacies shortly before she had asked him to move out.

A guy in the front row stood up. He wore a yellow guayabera, white shorts and Birkenstocks. He said, "Let's transform the room. Put the chairs in a circle. It's the divine form; it never ends. It's a symbol of completeness and the eternal. What do you think? Guys?"

The guy next to Lee had a jailhouse tattoo on the back of his right hand that said, "Born to Fuck Up." Under the words was a crude drawing of some goof lying on his back with a throbbing woody. It was the kind of tattoo you got from burning matchbooks and grinding up the carbonized match heads in saliva an laboriously sticking yourself with a straight pin Or letting your cell mate do it. Or maybe not letting him. Maybe he just did it. His way of making you one of the guys.

The leader said it was okay with him if they transformed the room. Nobody else objected. The tattooed guy next to Lee stood up, stretched, said, "What the fuck. I can do eternity."

He looked at Lee, possum face, gun sight eyes. He grinned. "My probation officer says I got to do a men's group, I do it. I got to get along with him. Men's group says I got to circle up, do eternity, what the fuck. Right?"

Lee nodded, right. Twenty guys arranged the chairs in a circle, scraping them on the beige tile floor in the basement of the Downtown Tampa Church of the Redeemer.

When they were seated again, nobody wanted to start. Not even the guy in the guayabera. Getting them into the divine form seemed to be his contribution for the evening. The men fidgeted or stared at their shoes or watched the paddle fans move the stale air around.

Lee stared at shoes. His own were flip-flops, the good kind with heavy rubber soles and leather uppers. His knees were disastrously fucked up from too many accidents on the gridiron of long ago, but he still had good, shapely feet. He thought so, anyway. He was wearing a pair of khaki shorts and a white rayon shirt. Loose, a good outfit for letting it all hang out with the guys. Talking about the innermost innermost. Hell, maybe there really was something left in there.

Most of the others favored the glove-thin, tasseled Italian loafer, their major element of self-expression being the color of the socks. There were a few pairs of heavy, no nonsense business shoes. One pair of Rockport loafers, the Birkenstocks. And the state-issue brogans next to Lee.

"Well, if nobody else wants to . . ." It was a guy in a starched, short-sleeved madras shirt and blue chinos. Cordovan Weejuns. He'd picked one of the colors from the shirt for his socks. Avocado green. Lee made him thirty-nine. Fraternity boy. Introspective. A research chemist or maybe a hospital administrator. The starch said something. Working wife? Anal retention?

The assistant pastor looked at the research chemist with casual gratitude. Silence didn't bother the churchman. He was about twenty-eight, blonde, with the beginnings of a monkish bare spot on his crown. He wore Episcopal black, his white clerical collar loosened. Message? No time to go home and change. Busy. Quasi-official here. The assistant pastor smiled and said, "Go on."

"Well," the research chemist said, "I think being a man's

got to be a lot of different things. A lot of them contradictory."

The Tattoo leaned toward Lee and whispered. "Contra-fucking what? Couldn't be anything easy, could it. Not for the twenty-first century?"

The assistant pastor shot them a look. It said, Gentle Jesus meek and mild wants you to shut the fuck up.

Lee smiled, leaned toward the chemist.

Most of the men around the circle watched the chemist earnestly. Interested in the way he'd started, glad it wasn't them.

The guy continued: "I think we have to be strong, but it's got to be a new kind of strength." He held up his hands and made a circle in the air. Drew a wavy line through it. "Sort of a Yin strength if you know what I mean." A few of them nodded. A few of The Nods didn't really know, but knew enough to fake it. One or two were openly baffled.

A new kind of strength, Lee thought. The strength to be openly baffled. Through clenched teeth, The Tattoo said, "I got a yen for some pussy right now. I don't know. It just come over me. Very sudden."

You learned to talk that way in the joint. Through a frozen smile, your lips not moving. Like Edgar Bergen with Charlie McCarthy on his lap.

The chemist said, "Because we've got this Yang down here . . ." He caressed the bottom of the imaginary circle in the air. His hands delicate, gentle. ". . . and it's getting stronger, changing all the time, threatening to change the shape of the whole. And we don't . . . I mean we want to keep the whole in symmetry. You see what I mean?"

Not so many nods this time. One or two faces demonstrating open skepticism.

The assistant pastor said, "Well, that's interesting. And it's certainly . . . Eastern. I wonder if any of you would care to add anything to that. Maybe put it in a more . . . Judeo-Christian context." He laughed. "Seriously, guys. Anything at all you want to say. This is about opening up. What we say here, stays here."

The Tattoo lifted his hand, looked at the legend written on it, flexed his fingers. "Say here, stay here," he sang through fixed teeth. "Got a ring to it."

A big guy on the other side, in jeans and Reeboks, shoved himself forward and said, "Aren't we getting a little philosophical?" The guy's face was tanned almost to the cancer point. Mutant right forearm a dead giveaway. Pete Sampris-itis. The guy was a club tennis pro.

"I mean, I thought we were here to talk about practical problems. I'm paying two thirds of what I make to a woman who hates my guts, and I got to beg her to let me see my kids. I drive fifty miles, and she says, 'Sorry, not today. They don't feel like it.' I go, 'Let me talk to them. Let them tell me they don't feel like it.' She goes, 'The judge, the fucking court told you I'm the one who says what they feel like. Now get your fucking truck out of my driveway before I call the police.'"

Lee did a revision. Too many rough edges for the country club. The guy got the deformed arm hanging drywall.

The guy pulled the Reeboks up under him and scuffed one toe with the other, rubbing his freckled hands on the thighs of his jeans. "That's the reality," he said. "You want to be a man in the twenty-first century, it's about moving your truck or not moving it." He looked at the assistant pastor, then at the research chemist whose hands hovered above his lap, maybe getting ready to make an imaginary shape in the air. A benzene ring of masculinity for the twenty-first century. A double helix that combined Rambo and Phil Donohue in dynamic equilibrium.

The drywall guy looked around the circle. Most of the men avoided his eyes. He subsided into his folding chair. The assistant pastor rubbed his bald spot and said, "I'm sure we all . . . honor your passion, your pain, though maybe we can't all say we have experienced it as intensely as you do."

Again, several men nodded. One or two mumbled about knowing the pain, experiencing it. The Tattoo grinned, raised his hand. Nobody recognized it. He lowered it, spoke anyway.   "Put the bitch in the truck, I say. Then you take her somewhere they don't hear anything, you know what I mean. Nobody around to hear anything. Show her your bank statements, talk to her about your cash flow problem, the kids. About being reasonable . . ." Tattoo smiled, looked around the room. "She don't listen, cap the bitch." He mimed a pistol shot, a heavy recoil. Grinned. One or two guys laughed, a few booed, several waved dismissive hands. Drywall shook his head slowly. Another lunatic. The assistant pastor said, "I don't think that was very productive, Benjamin."

"Well," Benjamin said, "what we say here stays here."

Lee was thinking that the assistant pastor and the parole officer would have a talk. About Benjamin's progress. About productivity. Acceptable forms of discourse in the basement of the Downtown Church of the Redeemer. Things like that. Benjamin stuffed his hands in his pockets and did a shoe check.

The guy in the guayabera said, "Well, at least we've sketched some points on a map here. We've got philosophy . . ." He looked at the research chemist who wasn't happy at being shelved under that heading, ". . . and we've got a very practical problem, a man and a woman in completely separate camps . . ." He looked gravely at the drywall guy, who nodded, content for the time being to camp where Birkenstocks had put him, " . . . and we've got, well, violence . . ." He looked at Tattoo and quickly looked away. ". . . an alternative that most of us would completely reject, I'm sure. Like I said, it's a map, and maybe we can use it to get somewhere."

The men around the circle nodded in sober affirmation. A reasonable summary. Made of the rough and ready stuff of a good straight talk. Men of good will, making the best of a bad situation. Planning the best of all possible worlds right here in the basement of the Downtown Church of the Redeemer.

Lee leaned back in his chair and let the future come into focus. The bronze plaque they would later put on the wall commemorating this place. The pilgrims coming here. Mostly shy young couples, happy and secure in their new shape, Philbo and Ramohue. Paying the modest price of admission and walking around commenting on what an unprepossessing place this basement was. How strange that the new millennium had begun right here.

" . . . so," the assistant pastor said, "we'll try to pick up in the same place next week. See you guys, same time. Have a good week."

The men got up, started to leave, remembered the chairs, scraped them back into straight rows. The assistant pastor called across the room, "Benjamin, can I have a word with you before you leave?"

Benjamin, The Tattoo. He stood next to Lee holding a chair. An "Oh, Shit" look on his face. He slowly put down the chair. Before turning to go, he said, "Fucking A. Whatever happened to free speech? That's what I want to know."

Lee smiled. "Don't worry, Big'un. After you leave, I'm gonna tell him I think you made one hell of a contribution. A breakthrough comment. Gave me my 'aha' moment."

The Tattoo stuck out his hand, fingers up. Gave Lee the power shake. .32 caliber eyes glittering. "Do it, man, really."

Lee said, "I will. I mean it."

Tattoo said, "You're a standup guy."

"Yeah," Lee said, "When my knee doesn't buckle.

Lee caught the assistant pastor in the parking lot. In a hurry. Removing the collar, tossing it in the front seat of his car. All around them men getting into their cars. A few of them picked up by wives with questions in their eyes. Who is this man, back from the twenty-first century?

Lee stepped up to the pastor's window. "Good meeting. At

least I thought so." He introduced himself. The Reverend Rogers thanked him for the good review. Lee offered a plea bargain for The Tattoo.

"I'm afraid there's not much I can do for Benjamin," the reverend said. "His parole officer sent him over on a trial basis, and he . . . flunked. Wouldn't you say?"

"I don't know. I think he was just embarrassed. Where he comes from, you talk like we did tonight, and they turn you into somebody's wife."

Rogers's jaw hardened. No references to jailhouse petting parties. Not in the parking lot of the Downtown Church of the Redeemer. "We?" the Reverend Rogers said. "You said we, Mr. Turner. I don't recall your making a contribution."

"It was only a manner of speaking."

"Well," Rogers said, putting on some fawn leather driving gloves, firing up his Saturn with a clerical plate. "In a manner of speaking, Benjamin is incorrigible. He's going back to the slam. He'll make somebody a good wife."

Lee stepped away from the car. He said, "All part of, what is it, being a man in the twenty-first century?"

"Something like that." Rogers smiled, thin and tight. "Something like that." Rogers got some rubber leaving the parking lot of the Downtown Church of the Redeemer.

Lee stood for a moment looking around at the humid night. A warm breeze from Tampa Bay, smelling of salt and rotting seaweed, tried to move the lank fronds of two Sabal Palms that flanked the entrance to the parking lot. Traffic soughed like surf out on Kennedy Boulevard.

Lee's soon-to-be-ex-wife, Miriam, drove up. She rolled down the window of her new Camry.

Lee walked over, leaned in. "Well," he said, "you could knock me over with a feather."

"Strong stuff, feathers," Miriam said. "What bends doesn't break." She smiled at him. The old smile of female knowing.

"What'd they do, show you the error of your ways?"

"A better question is, what are you doing here?" It was dark inside the Camry. Lee couldn't see her eyes, but he knew they were large and dark and mysterious, the eyes of all knowing. And he thought maybe they were laughing. But gently. She said, "When I suggested you give it a try, I didn't think you'd actually do it. I'm surprised." Her voice softened in a way that was hard to describe. Lee had tried to describe it to himself for twenty years. "I'm . . . pleased," she said.

He said, "You drove all the way down here in the middle of the night to see if I'd show up?"

The guy in the guayabera stopped on the other side of the Camry. Lee didn't like the look on his face. It was compassionate. The way you'd look at someone who was about to get bad news. Someone whose dog has been run over. Whose mother has to go to a nursing home. The guy was looking at him. Lee looked down at Miriam.

"No," she said, "that's not why I'm here."

The guy in the guayabera got in beside Miriam.

"Lee," she said, "this is Tom. Tom Easton."

Lee bent and looked in, inhaling Miriam's perfume and the good smell of the Camry's new leather seats. He watched the guy who had told them a circle was divine. Never ended. The guy who had asked if they could transform the room. The guy had one thing right. Some things never ended. Lee said, "How's it hanging, Tom, Big'un?"

Tom Easton smiled. A little uncertain.

Lee felt it coming. Getting big and serious. And not pretty. Certainly nothing to be proud of. He said to Miriam, "How come Tom didn't come around to this side. How come Tom didn't ask you to move over. Let him drive. That's what I used to do. Hell, I didn't even need to ask. We had it all worked out. You pull up, leave it running, slide over, I get in, off we go. Like that." He waited. He said, "Maybe Tom didn't want to ask me to move, you know, away from the window."

He looked over at Tom, whose embarrassment was big and all for Lee. Miriam was staring straight ahead, fingers tight on the leather-covered steering wheel. She said, "Goodbye, Lee. I'm glad you came tonight. I hope you'll think about what you heard."

Lee thought about Benjamin. The talk the Reverend Rogers and Ben's parole officer were going to have. What we say here, stays here. He said, "Tom, Buddy, that circular stuff was deep. I'm gonna give it some serious consideration." Tom smiled, slowly shook his head. It was ever thus. Lee stepped back. Miriam easing out the clutch.

Lee watched them go. Tom Easton's hand coming up to rest on the back of Miriam's neck.

After Miriam had driven away with Guayabera Tom, Mr. Havana Feelgood, Mr. Fidelito Naturale, Lee abandoned his old Ford in the parking lot of the Downtown Church of the Redeemer, walking fast in search of a shot of bourbon and a beer chaser. Something with no umbrella.

He started in the ACL Bar, a sort of working class place with pool tables and video games and softball teams smeared with red clay and talking loud about how Willy Billy could sureGod jack that horsehide puck over the palm trees. There were usually a couple of night-hawking reporters from the Tampa Tribune drinking lite beer and basking in safe seaminess. They seemed to get younger every year. All the president's children.

Lee knocked back a couple of generous doubles and headed out in search of a more bracing solitude. When the bourbons kicked in, he was on Nebraska Avenue counting the hexagonal sidewalk tiles and singing, "On the Sunny Side of the Street." The smell of the air reminded him of the nights of his youth. Sneaking out into the dark, quiet neighborhood, first with his dangerous pals, up to no good. Then leaving the company of boys to go knock on Miriam's bedroom window. The smell was complicated. It was heat from the octagonal paving tiles that had somehow pleased Tampa's city fathers seventy five years ago, bus exhaust fumes, the spice of oleander and ixora, and a too-sweet topping of jasmine.

Lee stopped in front of Maxie's. Maxie's was next door to a lap dancing club that was so minimal it had no name. The marquee said only, "XXXX. Nude Dancing." Maybe there was a kind of poetry in there. Another double Early Times and Lee would know.

Maxie's was home to the steady, no nonsense drinker. The guy who could pace himself, who arrived before noon and left when Maxie swept out at 2 A. M. In Maxie's you didn't have to pretend you were on your way somewhere, just stopping in for a quick one. You didn't have to pretend anything. It was cold in Maxie's, the better to suppress certain disagreeable odors. Well-brands were seventy five cents a shooter. Lee bellied up and ordered a double bourbon and a Bud. Maxie said, "We don't allow singing in here. You want music, feed the juke box."

Maxie's bad attitude was the stuff of legend. The cut-off Louisville slugger next to the cash register guaranteed Maxie's first amendment right to an attitude. Lee said, "I was singing?"

Maxie frowned and set up the shot and the Bud.

Lee said, "How'd I sound?"

Maxie took Lee's money and walked over to the register. He rested his right hand on the cut-off bat. "Like you had an operation." Maxie touched himself, low. "Like somebody hurt you. Down there." Maxie walked over with the implement and showed Lee the signature of Choo-Choo Coleman. The Choo had broken this particular bat in a Grapefruit League game in 1963. "It's a classic, all right," Lee said. "I defer to your greater understanding of the art of sound. You are a gentleman and a scholar."

"Drink up," Maxie said, "And shut up. We like it quiet in here." Maxie went back to the T.V. over the bar. A cable station. Two canvasback club fighters doing what looked like the bunny hop. Lee drank earnestly, quietly, signaled Maxie for seconds with a discreet cough, knocked back his refill and wandered next door. She was nude all right. And violent to the eye. Squat, lumpen and hugely uninterested in her own desultory movements, she did a clumsy grind to, "Do you Think I'm Sexy?" A revolving gel bathed her toady flesh in garish colors.

"The cover's five bucks. You gonna stand there or come in?" Your bouncer speaking. Two by four shoulders, black silk tank top, steroid-aggressive eyes. Hand out, palm up. Lee filled it with money and walked to the bar. Ms. Grind caught his eye, smiled, reached down and tangled her fingers in her pubic hair, gave it a tug in his direction. Lee gave back a courtly bow.

There were five other men in the place. Two college boys, hormonal enough to be mesmerized by Ms. Grind, a couple of downwardly mobile business types. Auto insurance underwriters? Purveyors of spray-on house coatings? A black guy in a white, short-sleeved shirt and horn rimmed glasses. Assistant principal on half-yearly testosterone retreat?

Lee asked for a bourbon shooter. The bartender, a grand-mother, told him they couldn't sell alcohol in a nude club.

"It's the law." She shrugged, disgusted. "Between the Bible thumpers and the femi-nazis it's all we can do to stay in business." She poured him a club soda. "You look like you got a load on already anyway."

Lee patted his shirt, trousers. Grinned. "It shows?"

The grandmother buried his five dollar bill in the register. "It shows," she said. She moved over to a small spotlight at the end of the bar and stood, back to the dancer, reading the dog racing form.

Lee took his club soda to a table in the back and sat watching the tired motions of air sex. He wondered who the woman imagined when she closed her eyes and those convulsive waves carried her out on a tide of guitar riffs and slow drums. Probably someone named Betty.

"Want a private dance?"

She was tall and trim with a Dorothy Hamil hairdo and wearing an emerald silk negligee. It moved on her like water. She had not appeared out of nowhere. There was a door, a dark back room. "Sit down," Lee said, "and explain that to me. The thing about a private dance." Lee looked at the chair next to him, but she walked around behind him and began massaging his shoulders. She knew how to play the muscles and bones.

After three minutes of picking his locks, she rested her chin on his shoulder. "Let's just say it's a hands-on experience." Peppermint breath. Halston. Both of them watching the dais where Ms. Grind was crescendoing to "Brown Sugar."

"She's pretty good," the woman behind him said. That tone women used when they said,   "She makes all her own clothes."

"You're better," Lee said.

"You haven't seen me dance. You've never even been in here. I'd remember you." She took his hand, pulled him out of the chair. "You're gonna remember this."

Idle Thoughts Janet Corso
Florida Mystery Haiku

Daily storms roll in,
thunder muffles gunshot sounds,
rain dilutes bloodstains.

Tip from the Cleaner Tracy Broussard
Florida Mystery Haiku

As the iguana
blends into the greenery,
bodies in the glades.

The Ballad of Polk and Tito Grant Balfour
Florida Mystery Haiku

Sun glints off his badge,
Tito's dope in his left hand,
as he draws his Glock.

"If that ain't the heat,
then it's the cocaine," Polk sneers.
"Sane folks stay up north."

Egrets overhead
soar precisely, pay no heed
to blood on sawgrass.

On the sixteenth hole,
gator trappers gut their prey,
find a human hand.

Stuck on the Turnpike
while evidence thaws and spoils,
forensics must wait.

Sergeant Polk retired,
bought a place on Bimini
. . .on a cop's wages?

Dade County Courthouse
makes Capone an example:
taxmen never sleep.

Counting days at Starke,
will Old Sparky work this time?
It did for Bundy.

84   ***Gulf*** Stream Cox

Half-Moon Kelle Groom

A girl at the bar had a wire coming out of her finger with a tiny cork at the tip—fingers bent toward earth, a V of black stitches like a nest in her palm. Her throat cut clean on both sides—*it didn't hurt, he'd sharpened the knife for three days.* She'd reached up, blocked his hand, her finger breaking over her vocal chords, past the knot of her hand he'd slit the other side too, ear to ear, except the very middle. They'd been broken up three months, she'd had a few beers, was sleeping when he'd broken her window, crawled in, was only going to kill himself, but since she was there, he sat on her chest, held her arms down, talked for ten minutes drunk, then cut her arm to show he could do it. When he left, she'd called 911—*I don't know how. All I could think was I want to be twenty-two.* Four doctors held her head up while they sewed her neck shut. *When they took out the staples I was scared my head would fall off. Could only lift it up with my hands. One ear's numb for good.* The bartender is sorry, buys us shots, kamikazis, little scryers like the green light they shine on sun-deprived kids. When the girl stands to leave, she's wobbly, and I'm nervous her head's not secure at her bright scar, a half-moon.

The Autopsy Melissa Fair

This one has an ocean in her lungs.
She might tell you how it is
to swim at night past the small breakers.
Past the buoys and out into deeper water.

She might tell you how the horizon disappears
and there is only black. How it's easy
to confuse up from down. Stars
from their reflections.

You want to tell her that every morning,
like clockwork, the sea spits out the sun.
You want to tell her this as you examine
the pale corpse she left behind.

You do not document the truth. That she heard
music. Her mother's voice singing softly
as she slipped under something dark
and permanent as ink.

Stormy, *Mon Amour* Vicki Hendricks

It's a breach birth, and soon as I see the tail slip out between my legs, I know I am caught. The doctors start to mumble about fixing "her deformity" — "replace rubbery gray hide with skin grafts" . . . "sculpt feet from the finlike appendage" . . . "separate muscles and bones to create legs." But I'm filled with pride and wonder at her beauty—and at how I widened the gene pool. "Don't touch her," I tell them. "She's perfect."

Roger figures it out on the way home from the hospital. "Jesus Christ," he screams. "It's Stormy's isn't it? You fucked that dolphin! You fucked that dolphin!" He glares into my eyes, and I can only worry about him keeping the car on the road.

"Only you, Cherie," he says. "Only a fuckin' French bimbo like you would think you could pass it off as my kid. I always said you'd fuck a snake— but fuck a fish? Christ." He stares straight ahead. His hands are bloodless on the steering wheel.

"He's a warm-blooded mammal," I tell him. "He loves me."

I sit back and look out the window. Roger shakes his head and makes a hissing noise between his teeth, and in my mind, I'm outta there. I'm sick of him telling me to use my brains instead of my heart, to "Grow up, grow up, grow up." He must have told me a million times that the world is a tough place and I better get used to it. He says I'd be found dead on the highway if he wasn't around to protect me. But it seems to me the only one I need protecting from is Roger. Before I got pregnant, he smacked me hard enough to put a tooth through my lip, and one time he dislocated my shoulder. He was so sorry I forgave him, but now I have a daughter to think about.

"Well, Cherie, I'm not stupid enough to support that fucking fish and let her father off the hook. Get your stringy little blonde French ass outta here. Take that thing and hit the road, before somebody finds out."

I don't bother to mention that she is a mammal also, a mermaid—or to explain how I fell in love with a dolphin. Roger is mumbling how he'd rather see the likes of her on a platter, but I ignore him, the swine. He's making it easy for me because I hate him more now than ever over the whole three years we've been married.

He wants me out by the weekend—tells me to charge a flight to my mother's in Quebec. But I figure the next day when he's at the restaurant, I'll hop a Greyhound for Islamorada. Asshole owns the car. All the time I'm asking myself why I handed my life over to a pudgy forty-year-old redneck who cooks animal flesh for a living. When I hitchhiked out of Canada, I never expected to become a redneck myself, a country girl in the sticks of Central Florida, taught everything by Roger. Now I'm twenty-one, legal, and have all the courage of a new mother to make a life for myself and my baby. I don't care about the rest of the world and what they might think about me and Stormy. We understand each other, and that's it. He trusts my judgment with every rubbery inch of his slick hard body, and with that to hang onto, I can make it work.

The next morning I wrap Mineaux's fin in a diaper and a wet blanket and slide her bottom into a plastic Winn-Dixie sack, so she's moist and comfortable for the long bus ride. The hundred bucks I've saved is in the diaper bag alongside canned tuna and sardines I scrounged from the pantry. It's a short walk to the station, and we're on the bus in no time.

I know exactly where to find the new father. He was taken out of the show for sexual behavior toward the female swimmers—really just me—and put in the isolation lagoon, where he had to learn tricks for his supper. I've been suffering with love ever since, and I can't wait to see him. Love, *mon dieu*. No stopping it. There's a legend that pink dolphins in Peru change themselves into human shape to seduce the village girls, make them fall in love.

The dolphins wear hats made from dried fruit to cover their blow-holes. Stormy never needed a hat.

I nurse Mineaux every time she wakes, napping in between until Key Largo. Then I hold her up to see the shining water, my eyes searching for dolphins from every bridge, even though I know he's not there. It's a beautiful place to start a fresh life. I get a cab from the bus station to Theater of the Sea. I'm not sure how to sneak Minny and me into the pool with Stormy, and I have a couple weeks to heal before I can get into the water, but at least I can show him his new daughter.

It's four o'clock when I walk through the gate. Only an hour left. I step right up to the window and charge the admission on Visa. I hope Roger hasn't thought of canceling. I tell them I don't want to swim, but they still make me pay to get inside. It's expensive. I wonder how long till I can get a job. Childcare might be a problem.

My spirits rise with the glimpse of Stormy's lagoon. I nearly skip across the concrete down the path and across the grass to the edge of the pool where I last saw him. There are no shows going on and no theater employees in sight. I search the surface of the water for the roll of his shiny gray head or a snort from his blowhole. I'm starting to worry he's been taken away when I catch a glimpse of him gliding along the glassy edge. He's fast and sleek. Sunlight glints off his head and makes him shine like mercury as he rolls and sinks. I'm not sure if he's seen me, but I'm in awe of his perfection and can't break the moment.

When his head emerges at the far side of the pool, I greet him with the series of squeaks I've learned. We don't understand each other's signals exactly, but the specifics aren't important.

Stormy dives under and makes a run. He surfaces in front of me and flings a set of drips off his nose that glint in the setting sun. I recognize his mannerisms. He's full of glee. I hold Minny to my side and squat on my heels as his gray vinyl face looms up. I tilt forward to touch him with my cheek. He catches the scent of the baby and sinks slowly back into the water, holding there without the flicker of a fin, his eyes bright and level with the bundle in my arms. I gently unwrap Minny, who is sleeping through all this, and set her down on the smooth rock edge in front of him. Her upper body skin is pink and soft, but her tail is thick tough hide, the best combination of both of us. She opens her eyes and begins to squirm. The black in Stormy's eyes deepens. I can feel his love and wonder welling up around us.

We're the perfect family, even if a photograph wouldn't show it. He nudges Minny with his beak, and I think he wants me to put her into the lagoon beside him. It worries me, in case I'm misinterpreting his intentions. I look at his upturned face, his snout making an upward jerking motion, same as when he wants fish, but there's love in his eyes, unmistakable. He knows he's the father and he wants to see her. He holds still a little ways out, in the calm lapping of wavelets. I lower her slowly and put her tail into the water a few inches. She isn't used to the temperature. Her fin pulls up and she looks at me with her face scrunched and starts to cry. I gather her, wet tail dripping against my body, and look around to make sure we are still safe.

Stormy hovers impatiently. "Just wait a few days, *mon amour*," I tell him. I'm afraid. I want to be able to get in with her. I know he's hurting for a touch, but I rewrap her. She's so tiny, and he can be a little rough. She squirms and nuzzles to nurse, so I slip my shirt up and she goes at it while Stormy watches with a father's love. I can see how much he wants to flop up on the grass beside us, and he has the strength to do it, but he holds back. When Minny dozes off, I set her down behind me, with the blanket bunched up under her head to keep her comfortable, and crawl back to the edge. I lie down so my head is close to the water. Stormy has been watching from somewhere under the surface and he raises up and rubs his face against mine, over and over like a cat, only more primitive, and stronger. I ache to get in the water with him. Ever since I met him that's where I want to be.

I put my arms around his round, smooth shoulder area and hold him, touch one finger to the rim of his blowhole, and stroke it gently like he enjoys. The sun is low and the air still. Minny is peaceful. I would be happy to stay like this forever.

"Park closing" blares on the loudspeaker and startles me. I sit up and glance around, but there's nobody in sight. I dry my arms on my shorts as Stormy watches from a few feet out. He waits there and I blow him a kiss, pick up Minny, and walk back along the path. I look over my shoulder every few steps so he knows I really don't want to leave.

I have to be careful, so I only bring Mineaux back once in the first week. I don't put her in the water, although she already takes an interest in it and reaches out toward Stormy. "Da Da," I tell her. "That's your Da Da." She might have the instinct to swim from birth, but I'm not healed and I want to wait till I can get in, just to be sure.

Lucky for me, right away I get a job at Lorelei's down the road. It's a nice dockside restaurant with a giant mermaid out front to attract attention—a colossal Mineaux. I get out of the motel I've been charging and move into a tiny apartment across the street from the restaurant, for rent by the week. Lorelei's agrees to let me work lunch and early afternoon. People are nice in the Keys, helping me work everything out. That way I can leave Minny during her nap and get a free meal a day, besides saving enough tips to pay the rent. My only expenses are diapers, the expensive admission, and a little food. I don't like leaving her alone, but she sleeps sound and I can't think what else to do. Two times the next week, I get her up after work and walk her over to see her papa. It's almost all the life I need. I don't miss Roger.

After two weeks I feel safe to get into the water. I have no way to tell Stormy why I haven't joined him sooner, but it's one of those things he accepts on trust. Never a complaint out of him. On the first night I can swim, I wear my bathing suit under my shorts, and when I stand and peel off the shorts, he lets out a throat full of wild high-pitched whoops. I have a little extra stomach on me, but one of the best things about Stormy is that he always thinks I'm beautiful. I slide in next to him in the cool water, and for the first time since the day we met, I wrap my arms around his body, the supple hardness no man can compete with. He's able to change the texture of his hide according to his mood, and he turns himself into velvet, sliding around and nudging across me with his catlike grace. He puts his erection under my arm—a touch like chamois over steel. He tows me around in his circles of glee until I get dizzy and let go.

I want to take my suit off, but I don't dare. If Minny starts to cry, someone might hear, and the staff will come running. I have to be quick. I hug that thick smooth hide and cling to Stormy's satin underbelly, my legs around the curve of his back, feet locked over his side fins. He nuzzles me and brings out his flat gray tongue, letting it rest across his mouth. I twist around his head, swiping his tongue across my shoulders, sending tingles down my back. I yank my top down and lower myself till his tongue is on my nipples, and his mouth covers my whole chest. I fasten myself tighter against it, feeling the hot rush I've longed for, his mouth and tongue like smooth rubber and fine suede nearly swallowing my chest.

I glance behind me. We're at the far end of the spit of land and so far nobody has wandered back after the last show, but it's still a risk. I find his erection again with my foot and rush his foreplay. It's a spike I can stand on with no problem, but I have no fear when I pull my bottoms aside and slip myself down over it as he rises under me, stretching me to my limit. He lies on his back to let me take control and holds level in the water while I work myself up and back, my own moisture making me more slippery than he is. The water warms up around us with the heat of our feelings. I hold him close, my face near his huge clear eye, like a crystal ball, as I feel the orgasm building inside my whole body. I let loose. Sky and water blend into a sparkling blur. Stormy holds still, tilted in the water, his fin waving slowly under us to keep my head above the surface, while I stay locked around him and float in a daze against his pure gray body.

Voices coming from down the path shock me back into the world. I scramble to get out, dress, and pick up Mineaux. A man and woman smile as they come to stand beside us and gaze at Stormy in his pool. They have no idea what they missed, but I'm shivering in my wet clothes and feeling the effects of a lucky escape.

A month passes fast. Stormy and me are the happiest couple I can imagine. Minny has grown double the size expected for a normal baby, and I feel safe to put her in the water. It's July, plenty warm, and one night I dip her fin to the hips. Her face shows surprise, but I make happy noises until she coos. Then I lower her waist-deep, level with Stormy's face on the surface. He nudges her side like a kitten, and she puts her pink baby fingers flat against his skin. He makes a soft squeak in his throat, and she answers him with a sound I can't imitate. She smiles. It's an instant connection. "Mineaux loves her daddy," I tell him. He hovers there, not making a sound, but his eyes are keen on her. We're just like a real family, except there's no yelling, no hitting, and no money problems to worry about. I glance behind me. Nobody watching, but it's time to go.

On the next visit, a few days later, I hold my breath and dip her face. She screeches, blinks, and opens her eyes wide as I bring her up. Instinct kicks in. Her arms flap and her tail pulsates so strong I can barely hold her. Stormy nudges my arm and I know he's saying to let her go. I'm not ready so soon, but I can't let them miss this moment. I take a breath, ready to plunge in beside her, and let go of her waist. She takes off on a straight path just under the surface of the water. Her arms streamline to her sides and she pumps to her own rhythm across the lagoon. Stormy is stunned for a second, but then he's by her side, gliding and watching as she surfaces for air, her face glowing with a baby smile I know isn't caused by gas. They begin to play, circling each other, Stormy letting out his most joyous shrieks and Mineaux rising up like an angel from the water, able to stand on her tail beside her father. They race in the glow of sunset. It's beautiful. My heart is bursting with love. I'm straining over the edge, enjoying their special bond, and there's only the slightest pinch in my heart because I can never share in their world completely.

After a few minutes, I get in and try to swim with them. They help me to overcome some of my human weakness in the water, holding me between their sturdy skins at the right angle for a smooth ride. I learn to pulse my legs and keep up with the help of a tiny arm on one side and a fin on the other.

It would be a fantasy come true, if we didn't have to beware of the rest of the world. As I take her out that night I see the sadness in Stormy's face, the slight downturn of his mouth. The scary thought that he wants me to leave Minny with him runs through my head. I know that he's lonely and unhappy doing tricks all day for his food in that small lagoon, and we are the only thing in his life he cares about. He's beginning to look lean and pale, even though he always has that built-in dolphin smile. His eyes are dull and his head is breaking out in small bumps. I know that dolphins can commit suicide by closing their blowholes and refusing to breathe, and I'm worried. He's suffering. I read it in his eye that he wants her there, but I can't leave her.

I'm walking past the office with Minny on my hip, headed to the exit, when a man steps out in front of me. He has a mean look on his face, and I know he's seen me several times. I'm sure there's been talk from the staff about me and my hanging around. I make the choice to defy him even before he can get any words out.

"I'm reporting you to the police," I say. "You've got a dolphin in here against his will, and it's cruelty to animals."

He shakes his head and frowns. "We've had nuts like you here before—cutting our gate, trying to free the dolphins. The police are on our side."

I hold Minny tight against me. "I belong to FETA," I say. "We're not well known like PETA, but we protect the fish in this universe. We're tough."

"Dolphins aren't fish," he says. He walks past me laughing.

"I know that," I yell. "We protect them too."

He looks back at me and his eyebrows go up, like he thought he heard words come out of my mouth, but decided it's only mosquito buzz. I turn toward the exit to get out of there with the baby. Right then a light comes on in my brain. It's as dim as a nightlight, but there's enough glow to see that all my life I've been a push over, somebody to ignore or boss around, and it's my own damn fault. I never stand up for myself, just run away from trouble and get nowhere. I've spent the last two months living like Stormy was going to raise up on his hind fin and swoop me over some threshold and into my dream world. But it's up to me to make a life for myself, my lover, and my daughter. Soon I'm going to get caught and jailed—and if they find out about Mineaux, she might become a test subject—a million bad things could happen. Nobody will ever understand me and Stormy. I have to remind myself that this relationship—so natural to me—is extreme to the rest of the world. I've been getting weird looks from the staff for a while. It's time for me to do something.

I watch the guy as he goes into the office. If he reports me I could get banned from the grounds. I have a feeling there's going to be trouble, and I need to get Stormy out of there fast before I get cut off or his condition gets worse. I think it's from nerves, caused by the sadness that comes from seeing what life could be for us if we had our freedom. He's helpless and hopeless.

I leave the park before anything can happen, but I know the man can identify me. I'm telling myself—as Roger would say— "Put your blonde brain into overdrive." The thought of Roger is fire in my head. I'll make a plan to beat them all. It's just one chain link fence that separates Stormy from the open water, and all I have to do is cut a dolphin size hole. Then I can follow him down the Keys and find a new place to stay where he can visit whenever he wants and roam the ocean like he's supposed to naturally. For the first time in my life, I realize that sometimes it's right to break the law—and this is the perfect occasion. Tonight is the night of the full moon, so it's my best chance, for reasons of light and luck, to get Stormy out.

I quit at work and tell them I'm sorry. I have no choice. I'll call about my check in a week. I'm ready to cry, so they don't ask questions. They were my first friends since I married Roger. I leave at four and cross the street to my apartment. I'm in a nervous hurry, because I have to rent a kayak before the guy closes, and then take a taxi to rent the bolt cutters. I put my key into the door to unlock it, but it locks instead. It seems like I forgot to lock it when I ran over during my last break. I turn the key back and step inside panicky, realizing that Minny has been there for a couple hours when anyone could walk in. Roger is sitting in the big chair by the window. He looks rougher than ever, with white stubble on his chin and his usual short gray hair now grown into a skinny ponytail. He's smoking a cigarette. A Bud is on the table next to him. "*Merde*," I say. "Fuck."

"Cherie, baby. I'm here to take care of you, honey."

My hands are shaking and I hold the door half open, dreaming that he could possibly slither back out. I'm unable to run because of Minny in the bedroom, and I'm unable to shut myself in with him. He stands up, walks over, and slams the door.

"How'd you get in, Roger?"

"Landlord gave me the key." He goes back to the chair. "What's a matter, sweetheart? I want to forgive and forget. I can't live without my little honey. I'm fallin' apart without you, babe."

I dart down the hall, not taking my eyes off him until I'm out of sight. I check on Minny and she's sleeping sound and her diaper and blanket are still wet inside the plastic bag. I close the door to the bedroom and take a big breath before dragging myself back to the living room. All I can think about is that I have less than an hour to get rid of him and rent the bolt cutters and the boat.

"How'd you find me?"

"Pooh. I knew you were here since you used that Visa card. Where else would you go anyway?"

I shrug.

"I wasn't thinking right when I told you to leave, babydoll. It's not like you cheated on me with another man." He laughs and shakes his head, but his eyes are flat. "This is special. It's a beautiful thing. We'll never have to work again. We've got a genetic miracle here, and they'll pay us big bucks and fly us all over the world. The kid'll be famous and so will we."

I sit down on the rattan couch. All I can think is to fuck him fast and send him off to some bar. He isn't going to leave until he gets it and feels back in control. We did the split up routine a couple times during the marriage, when I didn't have the sense to stay gone, so Roger figures I'm sucker enough to try us again. Then he'll be happy to head to the next beer light down the road and I'll head farther south with Stormy—maybe all the way to the Tortugas— and never have to see Roger again. I don't like cheating on Stormy, but it's my only choice, and since he can't ask questions, I'll never have to lie.

I smile and go over to sit on Roger's lap. His human stench closes around me, and I throw my head to his shoulder and fake a gag into a sob. "Hold me, big honey, I've been so lonely."

It's a nauseating idea to touch Roger's foul mouth, but I concentrate on closing off my senses and becoming a machine. He takes me into his grisly hairy arms and pulls my head back to start sucking at my lips. I taste and remember the hot sick slime of human spit passed from him to me, and I dig my nails into his back to brace myself while he sucks and slurps. He smears his sloppy tongue and lips over my face, until I feel clammy. He crams my mouth full of his tongue so the sharp bite of cigarettes stings the back of my throat. A beer burp thickens the air I breathe. I try to think of salty spray. I'll bathe myself inside and out before I ever touch Stormy and expose him to foul infected human mucus.

There isn't much time, so I swallow my disgust and pull my shirt over my head and step out of my shorts. Roger wedges off his shoes, toe to heel, and I squat to unbutton his shirt while he yanks off his socks. I slip the shirt off his shoulders, unhook his belt, and rip down his pants. He's ready to go, as big and hard as most humans can get. I put my legs around him, sit down on his purplish cock, and work myself up and down, applying all the pressure I'm able so he can't hold out for long.

"Oh, yeah, that's my little gal," he drawls. "Yeah, man."

I make some squeaky noises of my own, like I used to, but I'm spoiled by Stormy's fresh fish smell and smooth, thick steel-hard organ. This doesn't even feel like sex to me anymore, much less can I confuse it with anything called love. Roger's skin is hot and squishy and when he starts to sweat, I think I'll puke. He's fast, thank God. His ears go red, and he gives out that call like a bull elephant. I don't mean to insult the elephant, but Roger could do sound effects on Discovery. He's in and out of me in less than a minute. His head lolls and he leans back to doze in the chair. I take his hand. I can't leave him there with Minny, and I need to lock up and get a move on.

"Honey, I have to go back to work. There's a nice place down the road where you can wait for me. Beer's much cheaper than at Lorelei's—almost free. Unless you want to stay here and watch Minny? She might wake up with a dirty diaper and then you could change her for me and give her some sardines."

He opens his eyes and lets his jaw drop, then makes a smacking noise in his jowls. "Yeah, toots. I'll take your first sug-gestion. I'm pretty thirsty after that workout. Mmm, mmm. You're one sweet little thing."

His ass rises off the couch in an instant, like I knew it would at the mention of childcare, and he pulls on his clothes as fast as I've seen him move when his burgers were burning on the grill. I watch him walk down the sidewalk, and he makes a turn into the driveway where a car is parked. It's a new one. He's been spending money, probably counting on Minny as a gold mine.

I put on my clothes and check her. She's sound asleep and I can only pray she stays like that. I take the two-day's tips I've saved and my laundry quarters and my driver's license, in case they require some kind of security. It's a hot walk the short distance to the kayak rental, and I sweat my way down the street, moisture pouring off me from rushing and planning a lie. No other way. I can't move Stormy before dark, so I'll have to rent the kayak for an hour and steal it, at least temporarily. It's the only way I can get to the gate and cut it. I never did anything like this before.

It's a young guy, smoking some herb, and he lets me pay for one hour and takes my expired driver's license as a deposit without even looking at it. It has my right name, but I intend to bring back the kayak the next day anyway. I'll just have to pay off the bill gradually. I take my life preserver and get in and paddle out of sight of the rental guy, to a piece of land alongside the park, on the other side of the fence. I tie up to the overhanging mangroves, nice camouflage. I just have to take a chance that nobody will wander over there and take the boat. I have to leave a lot to fate, but I know it will work because I'm doing the right thing.

I walk back to the road and cross to the Tom Thumb grocery. I call a taxi and wait. It's only 5:30, so I'm okay so far. The time stretches to 5:50 by the time the cab pulls in, and I'm getting frantic thinking of how long this is going to take, Minny all alone, and Roger less than half a mile away.

I tell the driver to wait while I go into the rental place for the cutters. Behind the desk, the man looks at me odd, like he knows I'm up to something, but it's the Keys after all, so he doesn't say anything. I fill out a form and leave the Visa as a deposit. I don't know if I'll be able to return the cutters, so Roger will have to take care of the bill when it comes. Lucky for me he decided to make his fortune on Minny and never cancelled my credit. If it wasn't for Catholic school upbringing, I could have used the card plenty to my advantage, but those nuns just never let loose. I feel them grabbing at my ankles now, even as I keep on moving in what I know is the right direction in the long run.

The taxi driver turns to look, but I drag the bolt cutters onto the seat and tell him to take me back to the Tom Thumb. I think he's on to me too, but I don't give a rat's ass, as long as he doesn't try to stop me. I have him drop me near the path to the water. I hand him my last four dollars and change, and it barely makes the fare and a small tip. He hands me a dollar back. "You might need this, girlie."

I smile and thank him. I don't know what I'll do with a dollar, but it's good will, and that pumps up the hope in my heart and brightens my face into a smile as I swing the bolt cutters onto my shoulder and shut the door.

I walk the short distance to where I tied the kayak. I smear my arms and legs with jungle-strength Deet I brought for mosquitoes. I climb into the plastic boat and drag the cutters from shore and plunk them between my legs. At this moment it occurs to me that I might not be strong enough to cut the chain link fence that jails Stormy. I have no idea how much muscle it'll take. But I have no choice. I tell myself I can do it. I will do it. It's right. It's good for everyone.

I dip my paddles and ease out on the silvery surface, following my long skinny shadow over dark water where grasses grow and unfriendly sea creatures are, no doubt, lurking. I have maybe a mile to paddle around the point and into the area of the manmade lagoon where Stormy is captive. The last rays of the sun are warm on my back and I glide slowly, not wanting to reach the gate until dark. My mind is racing with thoughts of Roger so nearby and Minny probably awake by now, hungry and wet with urine that could turn her luminous scales to the dull gray blisters, her version of diaper rash. She's delicate that way, despite her hardy appetite and advanced swimming ability.

I reach the edge of Stormy's lagoon while it's still light and tie up under the mangroves to wait. The mosquitoes thicken with the night, but finally the moon comes up like a mother-of-pearl saucer, lighting my heart with hope and courage. I make my way to the chain-link barrier where my love waits. I hear his blow three times before I see him. He senses my presence on the other side of the spit of land and waits, probably wondering why I never came to see him at my usual time and spot.

As I round the corner to the high-fenced area, he rears up and looks me in the eye through the links. I reach two fingers inside and caress his silky nose and purse my lips to kiss the smooth tip. Under his gaze, I lift the bolt cutters, which are heavy just to hold, and put the pinch on a piece of chain-link at surface level. I use all my strength, squeezing the handles hard and getting nowhere. I take a breath—one, two, three—a hard punch, all I've got. I feel the blades bite, and the link snaps. I'm ecstatic, yet there are many more to go. I'll need to cut a big door to peel the fence back far enough to fit Stormy, but now that I've done one link, there's no stopping me.

I crouch low in the kayak to get the right angle, resting after each effort. I work myself into a sweat fast. It takes all my strength each time, and my arm muscles are shaking by the time I'm a third of the way. I can't let Stormy see, but I'm crying silently. I'm worn down and sick with fear thinking of Minny at home and it's nearly midnight. I can only hope Roger found some drinking buddies to keep him out late. It's the Keys, I remind myself, so that's a given.

I have to get into the water as I work lower, taking breaths and going under when my arms can't reach. I'm cold and shivering, even though the water is probably above 80. Finally, I make the last necessary cut and try to bend open the door I've created. It's tough. I climb back into the kayak, and wedge the nose in the open space to widen it, and swing the boat against the cut flap, crushing it against the immovable part of the fence. I smash the boat into it a few times to make sure the crease will stay, and Stormy will have plenty of room so not to scratch himself swimming through. I pull the boat out and back off, giving him space to make his break for freedom. He lifts himself to his tail and takes a look through the fence before making a move.

"Let's go, sweetie," I whisper. I'm panting from excitement and exhaustion, my teeth chattering with cold. I motion with my hand. "Swim through the hole." I know he doesn't understand my words—not like anything he's been taught—but he can see that his way is clear. I don't know why he's hesitating. He must not realize that somebody could find us at any second and close us off forever. I wish I brought a fish or two to lure him out faster.

Stormy sinks under the water and I think he's ready to shoot on past—still he waits. His eyes are wide open, but dull with the ill health that's been creeping over him. I wonder if I'm too late and he's weak. Maybe he's scared to leave his daily portion of dead fish. He hasn't survived on live fish for years and can't know that I'll keep him supplied. He floats silent and still. His eyes look from me to the hole and back again, but there's no flicker of motion.

I plead. "Sweetheart, go, go, go . . . . Please. Stormy, *mon amour*, swim . . . Come with me. We'll live together—in freedom, *cheri*— with our baby." *Plût à Dieu!* . . . I flop off the boat and swim through the opening and grab his top fin. I kick with all my strength and try to pull him forward, but the fluttering of my skinny legs, in comparison to the churning power of his mighty tail, is nothing but sound and splash. I kick and pull and kick until I wear myself out. My face slips underwater. As I lift myself for a breath, I choke, and Stormy puts his fin under my arm and boosts me up. I quit coughing and start to sob. He's not going anywhere, ever. He's too well trained.

I hang there on Stormy, crying and shaking, while he rests solid as a mountain in the wavelets. For the first time I wonder if he has ever shared the hot sharp pain of unfulfilled love between us, the need to be together or die that made me put my soul to the test and rise above my ordinary self to commit this deed. The sudden cold dawn of awareness is terrifying. I want to sink below the surface and stop breathing like he can do, never face the air and the world again. It's clear that he has never experienced the passionate longing I've read in his eyes. He has never loved me in human terms—and I am an idiot.

I gain back my senses and realize that I have to go home to Mineaux, but I can barely pull myself into reality. I look for the kayak, but it's drifted away. I can't spot it across the vacant moonlit water. The park will be locked if I go that way, and it's a long walk back around the point to the road, but it's the only choice. I've stolen the kayak and the bolt cutters and lost them both—I'm a criminal with no money and no reason to live—and a crippled child to care for.

I swim out through the fence and turn back for one last look at Stormy. He's waiting and watching, as he always does when I leave. I don't know what is inside his brain. I never did. I'm freezing and weak, but I breaststroke down the long line of fence toward a shallow place where I can climb out. I see moving lights in the distance and figure they're from the road, a road I had hoped to go down and never come back.

One set of lights moves in a different direction, and as I swim, it seems that this might be a car driving toward me on the point of land that I have to walk down. I pass the last piece of fence and climb out onto the rocky edge. It is a car, getting closer. I lower myself back into the water to hide. It must be the police. In a few minutes the car pulls up and stops. There are no beacons, only headlights. I realize the perimeter fence is blocking the way from here. The door opens and a man gets out. He walks to the fence and his face catches moonlight—it's Roger.

He looks into the nearest pool on the other side of the fence and then sits down on the hood. Somehow he knows I'm here. He's planning to wait. I don't know what to do. I can try to swim past him without making a sound and hide in the brush until he drives past me. I'm ready to give it a try when I hear crying. Good God. Minny's in the car. I haul my dripping self up the rocks. Roger sees me and stands watching as I take a few steps and stop to cough.

"I knew it," he says. "Blonde French bimbo."

"I need to get the baby, Roger."

"I was in the Tom Thumb buying cigarettes. Saw you get into a taxi with bolt cutters."

"Oh." I twist my hair and wring it behind me, walk past him, and open the car door. Mineaux smiles at me from her baby-seat on the floor. I reach for her and hold her against my shivering wet body, taking her warmth, knowing she doesn't feel the cold.

Roger stands looking down at me. "I thought maybe you were picking up tools for your boss, so I went on back to the bar, but I couldn't quit thinking about it. It was midnight by the time I got back to your place. I knew exactly what you were up to."

He purses his lips and nods his head—like he's so clever, and I'm such a loser. He's half right. "What kind of a mother are you anyway, leaving your kid all night without food—and nearly dry? I changed her, fed her, and re-wet her blankets. I don't know what you'd do without me."

"You changed her?"

"Protecting our future, honey. Don't expect it to happen again."

I look at his face of broken blood vessels and stubbly gray chin, and I sob into Minny's blanket, with nothing left except the painful knowledge of my lunacy. Roger motions me into his arms, but I turn and scoot into the car and close the door. He gets in on the driver's side and flips on the heat to warm me up. I'm going with him, and that's all he cares about. If I have to share Mineaux with the world, maybe I should. I don't know what Roger will expect from us, but I know all that Stormy never had to offer. The world is a tough, lonely place, and I can only hope to survive.

Sex and Dolphins in the Sunshine State:
An interview with Vicki Hendricks Melanie Neale

Vicki Hendricks is the author of noir novels Miami Purity, Iguana Love,
Sky Blues, *and* Voluntary Madness. *She teaches college-level writing in
South Florida, and is known for her adventurous nature both on the page and
off. I read her bio on the sleeve of* Iguana Love *in a small used bookstore in
the Keys a few years ago, and I knew right away that I'd kill for the chance to
interview her. She read at the 2002 Miami Book Fair with her arm in a sling,
and I thought, "Here's a writer who actually spends time away from the
computer." Her adventures have included skydiving, living by herself aboard
a small sailboat in the Florida heat (without air conditioning), scuba diving,
rock climbing, and swimming with sharks.*

Thank you, Vicki. You kick ass.

∗   ∗   ∗

*When you hear the term "Florida Noir," what is the first thing that comes to
mind?*

The irony of it. The darkness of the Sunshine State. I thrive on
irony in my writing and maybe that's part of the reason I love
Florida. Most of my titles contain irony—*Miami Purity, Iguana Love,
Voluntary Madness.* The titles seem to have grown naturally from
the place. I don't think we have a different kind of crime or
insanity from other populated states, but our dark deeds are played
out against a background of warm beaches and glittering water,
with an expectation of infinite paradise. The original definition of
noir required a love triangle and betrayal, generally for money, but
lately anything dark gets the prestigious French term *noir*, so the
words *Florida Noir* leave the category open for the variety of styles
we have here, all with that great inherent irony.

Is it some sort of cross between Southern Gothic and Florida Mystery/Thriller, or do you think the genre has sprouted up completely on its own?

Southern Gothic is definitely involved. Flannery O'Connor, Harry Crews, and Larry Brown come to mind as heavy influences on my own writing. South Florida adds contemporary chic, but I think a kind of gothic "horror" flows down through the middle of the state. Maybe that's part of what makes Florida Noir its own brand, different, say, from California style.

What did you read while you were developing as a writer? I know Miami Purity *has been compared to James M. Cain's* The Postman Always Rings Twice. *Are there any other books, noir or not, that influenced you?*

Postman and other works of Cain were the main influence of both the type of plot and the style of writing in *Miami Purity*. Cain's unique style of compressing passion and intrigue into so few pages is what I'm always trying to emulate. I was obsessed with reading Cain during my studies at FIU, after several years of obsession with Harry Crews and Charles Bukowski, and earlier with Hemingway, so all those are part of me. Also, I've always felt akin to the French existentialists. When I found out that Camus had used *Postman* as a model for *The Stranger*, I was thrilled, since that's what I had done in writing *Miami Purity*.

How do you feel about the word "genre" anyway? I hate to toss it around so much, especially when I know some people have an aversion to being dubbed "genre writers."

I don't have any aversion to the word—although nobody has ever said it to my face! Genre writing can be lousy or it can be literature. It all depends on how the subject matter is handled. We turn up our noses at the romance genre, but if we classified most of the literary writers, classic to contemporary, they would fall into that category, since fiction is nearly always about relationships. Formula stuff and poor writing have given the genre of romance a bad name among educated readers, and the same thing has happened in part to SF and mystery, but not so completely as to make being called a genre writer an insult. Of course, if people would just stop buying lousy writing, it would disappear, and then we wouldn't have to worry about the bad stuff getting lumped in with the good.

I just finished reading Voluntary Madness, *and one of the things that I enjoyed most about it was the sympathy you make the reader feel towards Juliet, the protagonist. She's caught in a destructive relationship, and she does things that most of us would consider to be way too socially deviant for our own tastes. Yet, when things work out so beautifully in the end, we're happy for her. Did you try to make the end uplifting for a reason, or did it just happen?*

Glad to hear you felt that way. I tried three endings for that novel and never could decide which one I liked best. I had one I thought of as the "popular" ending, another that was bleak, and then this one I chose that I felt was bittersweet. Maybe I should have gone with the "popular" ending since this novel was only published by Serpent's Tail and got very little distribution in the U.S. The bleak one was actually more my style, but the one I chose was more complex.

What should we expect from Cruel Poetry?

"*When* should we expect *Cruel Poetry?*" is probably the better question. This answer might sound like too much information, but I like to share what I've learned from the publishing business since I think readers want to know more about it, as dreary as the situation may seem at times.

I'm looking for a new agent on this book because my last agent was extremely negative on it. Noir, especially the sexual kind, is considered a particularly low seller right now in the U.S. Also, my low sales record is a major part of the problem. One agent told me straight out that he didn't even want to see the manuscript for that reason. Since my last few contracts have been in the very low range, the 10-15% agent fee doesn't seem worth the trouble to most of them. I'm told I need an agent who's "young and hungry." If a writer hasn't "broken out" as they say, after a few books, with around 20,000 sales or so, on one of them, the prospects for sudden big money are poor, and agents don't want to work that hard, since there are other much greater possibilities out there. I don't blame them, but I'm pretty sure that *Cruel Poetry* is my best novel, and even if I'm wrong, it's certainly in the same category as the rest, so having trouble getting an agent is disappointing. However, I'm proud of the book and don't have any regrets for the time spent. The numbers problem has been obvious for years, but the readers I have are enthusiastic with their appreciation—I get emails from all over the country and parts of the world—and some of my favorite writers love my writing, so I can't help feeling good about what I do. On *Cruel Poetry*, I might find a publisher by myself, as I've done in the past, or I might just publish outside the U.S. until the market changes. I'm working on a screenplay right now, as well as a book of short stories, so I'm not wasting time worrying about it.

In answer to your real question, *Cruel Poetry* is packed with sex, drugs, murder, and emotionally challenged characters. It's a "love pentangle" between a female prostitute and her obsessed male and female lovers, played out on South Beach; probably my darkest novel.

What do family members say to you when they read something like "Stormy, Mon Amour?"

Most of my family members don't read short stories, mine included. One of my sisters inspired the idea behind "Stormy" from the time she swam with the dolphins and told me about a really nice one, Stormy, who kept following her. I sent her the story, but she never made any comment and I didn't ask. She might have thought I'd defiled poor Stormy's good name. However, I heard from the editors of *Tart Noir*, where the story was originally published, that they got more shocked comments on that story than any of the others—and we're talking about a collection that doesn't flinch on raw situations. Apparently, people have idealized dolphins and mermaids, and writing about their sex lives is taboo. Wouldn't you know!

Sex. I applaud your bravery and honesty. How do female readers typically react to your female characters? I ask about female readers, because I think it's safe to assume that your male readers are thrilled.

Yes, when I get any flack about characters, it's about sex, and it comes from women. With pride I tell you that during its debut, *Miami Purity* was the number one book to be found on the floor in the stalls of the men's room in Borders! I mentioned this to a British interviewer, and he was astonished. He thought the Brits were the only ones still masturbating to print media.

Typically, women readers find my characters' sexuality and tough-ness to their liking; however, I have ignited some basic female instincts against me from a couple of horrified women at the *Miami Herald*. I guess I don't try to please everyone, and these reviews were so overblown that I'm sure they got more attention than a mediocre or even good review would. The only problem is that, of course, those are the reviews my friends see!

Again, about sex. Your story "ReBecca" is published in the Best American Erotica, 2002 *collection. Has your writing always been sexually charged, or was this something that you worked to develop?*

Funny thing, "ReBecca" has very little sex in it, but it's famous as erotica. It's my most published story, having been in five different places. Sex has always been the most important ingredient in my writing, from day one with the first short story I handed out in a workshop to be critiqued. And from that moment, it has always drawn controversy. I don't know if I keep putting in the sex because I enjoy exploring that area or if the controversy continues to fuel me. Probably both. At this point I'm getting a little bored with writing about normal sexual situations—but then there's always the twin or the woman and dolphin type variations. I have perverse taste obviously. Sex is the thing that interests me most, and despite the problems it causes with publishing and family, I don't plan to give it up.

Would you consider the world of erotica to be a good market for aspiring writers?

Probably not. Everyone always says "Sex sells," but it usually goes pretty cheap. For me, sex gets the writing noticed, but publishers won't promote it. There's generally very little sex in monetarily successful mysteries or mainstream novels. Susie Bright makes a living with her sexual writing and collections, but most of us are keeping our teaching jobs. Moral anxiety keeps erotica on the fringes, and also, like the romance genre, bad writing is very much in evidence, probably because literary value isn't of great importance to many of the readers. Actually, now I think the discussion of sex is becoming so everyday to young generations that graphic details will eventually, like violent ones, be seen as realistic parts of life and literature, as they should, instead of being called sensational and gratuitous.

I can't interview you without asking about skydiving and sailing and all the rest of your adventures. How important do you think it is for writers to leave their computers every so often?

For me, sitting in front of the computer is much more difficult than leaving it. I've heard of people who enjoy staying home to write, but I don't know any of them. Certainly there are a few thrilling moments of personal triumph at the computer, when something is flowing or works out surprisingly well—or seems to—but it always takes discipline to sit there until you've accomplished what you require of yourself in number of hours or pages. The discipline gets easier as the years go by because you're used to the tedious work, and you know it will lead to something positive eventually. In my case, many of my stories contain details that I could never have imagined or created without my adventurous activities, but in truth, by now I've probably stocked up enough material for a lifetime, and I would be better off, in many ways, to keep my ass in the chair.

Didn't you break your arm skydiving last year? How did you write with a broken arm?

You probably remember more about the 2002 Miami Book Fair than I do. I was heavily medicated and too bullheaded to stay home. People who knew me well were waiting with amusement to hear what crazy thing I would say next. When I was reading from *Sky Blues*, I had to keep reminding myself that the words *must* make sense because the book was published.

Actually, I didn't break my arm—I had shoulder surgery three days earlier for torn and dislocated bicep and subscapularis tendons, and other damaged connecting parts. My arm was yanked behind my body on a three-way exit from a plane—two guys I had a firm grip on launched themselves in different directions. It's a common exiting injury, as I've since learned. I've stopped doing the kinds of linked exits where this happens most often, but the truth is that skydiving in groups usually involves a lot of body contact, and every now and then something gets pulled or hit too hard.

I think the surgery kept me from writing for about a week when I was on painkillers, but after that I just typed with one hand for a month or so. It was slow going, but not too bad. Overall, the experience was interesting since I learned a lot about myself physically and mentally. Eventually I might be able to use some of the "material." I'm told that shoulder surgery is one of the most painful types, since there are so many nerves and connections in that area, so now I know I can handle it and other injuries that I might undergo. My recovery is nearly 100%.

I know you've written a book about skydiving, and you draw from your other adventures as well. Your website says you're working on a memoir. Can you tell me about it?

I've written some articles and used the skydiving to a great extent in *Sky Blues,* but the memoir is only in small pieces so far, adventures with zebras in South Africa, swimming with pink dolphins in Peru, as well as a variety of rock climbing and scuba diving stuff. I've been working on it, or saying I am, for at least five years, but I can't seem to get the voice right or decide on the structure. I could put together a collection of essays on adventure and travel, but that's been done so well so often–Randy Wayne White and Pam Houston, to name two great ones—that I want to do something different. I have a book length story in mind, but I'm just not ready to write it yet. I'm not comfortable getting into deep truths about my life. Maybe I still need to mature.

Nameless Lucille Gang Shulklapper

His body lies on shore   in pieces   the flesh   alligator-eaten
in dark and hungry   sleeps   his arm floats   in the canal
behind the banyan trees   teeth marks crunch   the bent wrist   angled
upward   bobbing on   rip-pulled waves   in the tilted moonlight

before his night-wandering sleep   in his bed on the banks
he stumbled   shoeless into the canal   cleansed caked mud
from his tee shirt   a spot of ketchup   his own stink

not crying out   when the beast dragged him   into the undertow
of   dodged cars   of waved front pages   of pocketing   the sell
road-weary in the Florida heat   of gulping the bottled sun   to sear
the pain of death of a marriage his little girl his brother his parents

not crying out   when the beast dragged him   into the undertow of
blueprints   of skyscrapers   shimmering love   a home behind
the banyan trees   baseball games   a little brother   a piggy bank

not crying out   when the beast dragged him   into the undertow of
his mother and father   rocking him to sleep   body fed   powdered
bathed   wrist bent   baby flesh   kissed   fingers counted

Contributor's Notes

Preston L. Allen, a recipient of a State of Florida Individual Artist Fellowship in Literature, holds an MFA in Creative Writing from FIU. His works have been published in *The Seattle Review*, *Crab Orchard Review*, *Drum Voices*, *GulfStream*, *Asili*, and *Brown Sugar: A Collection of Erotic Black Fiction*. He is the author of the short story collection *Churchboys and Other Sinners*, winner of the Sonja H. Stone Prize in Literature, as well as *Bounce*, *Come With Me Sheba*, and the mystery/thriller *Hoochie Mama*.

Grant Balfour, tabloid poet and bon vivant, was last seen leaving The Compleat Angler restaurant in Bimini in the company of two male witnesses described as "curiously fish-like" and "unpleasant characters." His current whereabouts are unknown, but he is expected to return to West Palm Beach shortly.

Tracey Broussard is the editor of the culinary anthology *Irrepressible Appetites*, and a former caterer. She holds an MFA in Creative Writing from FIU, and has been published in numerous periodicals. Her latest work is a memoir of her journey to black belt entitled *Jump! How High?*

Terri Carrion received her MFA from FIU. She is assistant editor of *Big Bridge*, an online magazine. Her poems have appeared or will appear in *Vox*, *Slipstream*, *Pearl*, *Mangrove*, *Hanging Loose*, *The Cream City Review*, *Jackmagazine.org*, *Paper Tiger* (Australia), *Street Miami*, *Mad Love* in the *Miami Sun Post*, *PoeticInhalations.com*, *Mipoesia*, and *Tigertail*. Other photos are forthcoming in *Jackmagazine.org* and *DeadDrunkDublin.com* (Ireland*)*.

Janet Corso is a Brooklynite (NY) by birth and Floridian by deliberate intent. She is a member of the Nova Southeastern University

Law School community and really, really, really enjoys writing.

Marlys Lens Cox is a sixth generation Floridian devoted to capturing what is left of old Florida with her camera. She graduated from Georgia State University with a MFA in photography. Her work is in museum collections and she has won numerous awards at art shows. She has done book covers and commercial work for Turner Broadcasting, AT&T, Emory University, Peachtree Publishers and for advertising agencies.

Silvia Curbelo is the author of two poetry collections, *The Secret History of Water* and *The Geography of Leaving*. Her poetry has appeared or is forthcoming in *American Poetry Review*, *Crab Orchard Review*, *Tiferet* and *Notre Dame Review*, and in the anthologies *Snakebird: Thirty Years of Anhinga Poets*, *Never Before* and *Norton's Anthology of Latino Literature*. A native of Cuba, Silvia lives in Tampa, Florida, and is managing editor for *Organica* magazine.

Melissa Fair's work has appeared in *Apalachee Review*, *Kalliope*, *X*, and will soon appear in *Bitter Oleander*. She performs regularly with an improv jazz/world beat/funk band, The Irritable Tribe of Poets, fusing poetry and musical soundscapes. Most recently they were commissioned to perform during the Salvador Dali Centennial at the St. Petersburg Dali Museum.

Joann Gardner is an associate professor of English at Florida State University. She directs Runaway with Words, a poetry program for at-risk youth, and is the associate director of Anhinga Press. Her poems have appeared in such journals as *Crazyhorse*, *Seneca Review*, *Tampa Review* and *Louisiana Literature*. She has held artist residencies at Villa Montalvo and the Blue Mountain Center.

Kelle Groom's first collection of poems is *Underwater City*. Her second collection, *Luckily*, is forthcoming from Anhinga Press.

Her poetry has appeared or is forthcoming in *Agni, Borderlands, Crab Orchard Review, Florida Review, Luna, The New Yorker, Poet Lore, Witness,* and others. She is the director of grants for the Coalition for the Homeless of Central Florida.

Vicki Hendricks lives in Hollywood, Florida, and teaches writing at Broward Community College. Her published novels are *Miami Purity, Iguana Love, Voluntary Madness,* and *Sky Blues.* Hendricks has contributed short fiction to several collections and periodicals, including "ReBecca," in *Best American Erotica 2000.* "Stormy, *Mon Amour*" first appeared in *Tart Noir,* a collection edited by Lauren Henderson and Stella Duffy.

David Kirby's latest collection of poems, *The Ha-Ha,* was published by Louisiana State University. He is the Robert O. Lawton Distinguished Professor of English at Florida State University; for more information, see www.davidkirby.com.

Christine Kling has spent over twenty years living on and around boats and has cruised the waters of the North and South Pacific, the Atlantic, and the Caribbean. Working as a charter boat cook and deckhand in the Virgin Islands, she earned her 100-ton U.S. Coast Guard Captain's license. Her articles and stories have appeared in many boating publications including *Cruising World, Motor Boating & Sailing,* and *The Tiller and the Pen.* She completed her MFA in Creative Writing at FIU in Miami, and Ballantine published her first novel, *Surface Tension,* in November 2002. Her second novel, *Cross Current,* featuring tugboat captain Seychelle Sullivan, was released in September 2004. Currently she is at work on the third novel in the series while working as a coordinator for the Magnet Programs of Broward County Schools in Fort Lauderdale, Florida.

Mark M. Martin is a writer/editor and amateur photographer.

His photos have appeared in *Street Miami* and *Big Bridge*. To see more of his photography, visit his Web site at www.fotolog.net/m_m_martin.

Barbara Mooney is a retired community college instructor who spent thirty years at St. Petersburg College teaching courses in composition, mass communication, and popular culture. She has a master's degree in English Literature (and is also ABD) from the University of South Florida. She is Chairperson of the Curriculum Committee and a member of the Advisory Council of Senior College at Eckerd College (an Institute for Learning in Retirement), and Vice Chairperson of the St. Pete Beach Library Advisory Committee. In her spare time she is an avid reader of mysteries.

Melanie Neale is an MFA student in the Creative Writing Program at FIU. She graduated from Eckerd College in 2002, with a BA in Creative Writing. In addition to writing fiction, nonfiction, and poetry, Melanie spends her time on and around the water, fishing and sailing. She is a U.S. Coast Guard licensed captain, and has published articles in several boating magazines. She lives aboard a twenty-eight foot sailboat in North Miami with her dog. Her work has appeared recently in the *Miami Herald Tropic Life Magazine*.

Abigail Purdy is a recent graduate of FIU's MFA program. She lives in Dayton, Ohio, with her husband, Steve.

Lucille Gang Shulklapper is a workshop leader for The Florida Center for the Book, an affiliate of the Library of Congress. Her fiction and poetry appear in *The Art Times*, *Common Ground*, *Curbstone Review*, *Slant*, and others. She is the author of two collections of poems: *What You Cannot Have* and *The Substance of Sunlight*.

Eric Vichich graduated from Eckerd College with a degree in Environmental Studies. An Environmental Specialist with a non-profit group in Tampa Bay, Eric works to restore Florida's natural ecosystems. His passion is nature photography. Eric hopes to inspire others to protect and preserve the natural and cultural resources of our planet.

Sterling Watson is the author of five novels, *Weep No More My Brother*, *The Calling*, *Blind Tongues*, *Deadly Sweet*, and *Sweet Dream Baby*. Watson is the recipient of three Florida Fine Arts Council awards for fiction writing and is a former fellow of The Virginia Center for the Creative Arts. His short fiction and non-fiction have appeared in *Prairie Schooner*, *The Georgia Review*, *The Los Angeles Times Book Review*, *The Fiction Quarterly*, *The Michigan Quarterly Review*, and *The Southern Review*. He has co-authored several screenplays, two of them based on his novels, with novelist Dennis Lehane. He is Director of the Creative Writing Program at Eckerd College and has taught at the University of Florida and the Florida State Prison, at Raiford. He received his BA degree from Eckerd College and his MA degree from the University of Florida.

$3000 PRIZE
& PUBLICATION

The *Prairie Schooner* Prize Series – an annual competition for a **book of short fiction** and a **book of poetry** – will be published by the University of Nebraska Press.
Winning authors will receive $3000 (including an advance from UNP).

Prairie Schooner welcomes full-length manuscripts from all writers, including non-US citizens writing in English, and is open to those who have previously published books, as well as first manuscripts.

Manuscripts with a $25 entry fee, should be mailed with a postmark between **January 15 and March 15, 2005** to:

Prairie Schooner Prize Series in poetry/short fiction (pick category), University of Nebraska–Lincoln, 201 Andrews Hall, PO BOX 880334, Lincoln NE 68588-0334

Check out our website:
www.unl.edu/schooner/psmain.htm
for guidelines, information, and updates

Prairie Schooner

What company do you *keep*?

PLEASE HELP!

Every day deserving poems, short stories, interviews, and essays wander the streets looking for a few pages to call their own. We here at *Gulf Stream* desperately want to give these worthy works of literature a safe haven. Believe it or not, YOU can make a difference! Every little bit counts.

Become a Friend of ***Gulf*** Stream today!

Please make checks payable to Gulf Stream.

-SUBSCRIBE TODAY-

Don't miss another issue of
South Florida's Literary Current.

1 Year - $15__

Current Issue - $8__

Back Issues - $5 each__

Name:_____

Address:_____

_____

City/State:_____Zip:_____

Join our email list for up to date contest information!

Email:_____

Send Check and Order form to:
Gulf Stream
Department of English
FIU - Biscayne Bay Campus
3000 NE 151st Street
North Miami, FL 33181

Creative M✦F✦A Writing

FLORIDA INTERNATIONAL UNIVERSITY
MIAMI, FL

One of the top ten Creative Writing Programs in America as listed in "Who Runs American Literature?" in the *Dictionary of Literary Biography*.

For information:

Creative Writing Program
Florida International University
Biscayne Bay Campus
3000 N.E. 151st Street
North Miami, Florida 33181
Tel: 305.919.5857
FAX: 305.919.5734

Internet: http://w3.fiu.edu/crwriting//
E-Mail: standifo@fiu.edu

Gulf Stream

GUIDELINES FOR SUBMISSION OF MANUSCRIPTS

Gulf Stream is interested in publishing quality fiction, poetry, and creative non-fiction. Manuscripts should be:

1. Typed on white 8 ½ by 11" paper and must be accompanied by a self-addressed stamped envelope. Submissions can either be submitted by postal mail or via email by visiting our website at: http://w3.fiu.edu/gulfstrm
2. Please do not submit more work if we are still considering your previous submission.
3. Do not query; we are currently accepting unsolicited submissions.
4. Include a cover letter with some biographical information.
5. Submissions must be previously unpublished.
6. Our payment is 2 copies, a year's subscription, and 2 gift subscriptions.
7. We hold first serial rights for the material we publish, with the copyright reverting back to the author upon publication.
8. We do accept simultaneous submissions, but this must be stated in the cover letter.
9. **Reading period: September – January 1**

WE READ:

POETRY – no more than 5 poems
FICTION – no more than 5,000 words
NON-FICTION – no more than 5,000 words

We encourage you to purchase a sample copy for $5.00 to familiarize yourself with the type and level of work we publish.

Check our website for upcoming contests!
http://w3.fiu.edu/gulfstrm/Gulfstreaming.HTM

Please address all correspondence to:

Gulf Stream
English Department
FIU Biscayne Bay Campus
3000 NE 151 Street
North Miami, FL 33181-3000